TABLE OF CONTENTS

This section includes the following:

PRINCIPAL DIAGNOSIS CODING RULES

On the following pages, the key principal diagnosis coding rules from the most recent ICD-9-CM Official Coding Guidelines for Coding and Reporting (OCG) for the selection of the principal diagnosis (PDX) have been summarized to assist coding and CDI professionals in selecting and assigning the principal diagnosis.

The authoritative sources for coding guidance should be reviewed and referenced routinely for specific situations and circumstances to ensure accurate coding. These include:

- ICD-9-CM Classification
- Official Coding Guidelines for Coding & Reporting (OCG)
- AHA *Coding Clinic*

Note that the instructions and coding conventions in ICD-9-CM Volumes I and II (soon to be ICD-10-CM) take precedence over the Official Coding Guidelines, which in turn takes precedence over *Coding Clinic*.

Definition of Principal Diagnosis:

> "That condition established after study to be chiefly responsible for occasioning the admission of the patient to the hospital for care." OCG Section II.

Also, consider ***WHY*** the patient was admitted to the hospital and could not go home.

The condition (or at least some signs or symptoms referable to the condition) must be present on admission. In some cases it may be several days before the provider arrives at a definitive diagnosis. This does not mean that the condition was not present on admission.

Per OCG page 1, "The entire record should be reviewed to determine the specific reason for the encounter and the conditions treated."

I. Two or More Diagnoses That Equally Meet the Criteria for Principal Diagnosis

"In the unusual instance when two or more diagnoses equally meet the criteria for principal diagnosis **as determined by the circumstances of admission, diagnostic workup, and/or therapy provided** and the Alphabetic Index, Tabular List, or another coding guideline does not provide sequencing direction, **any one of the diagnoses may be sequenced first."** OCG Section II.C.

Examples:

Patient admitted with CHF and pneumonia. Patient given IV Lasix and IV antibiotics. Either may be sequenced as the PDX.

Patient is admitted to the ICU with respiratory failure due to severe exacerbation of COPD. A pulmonary consult is called. Treatment includes IV antibiotics, steroids, oxygen, pulse oximetry, and aggressive respiratory therapy modalities. Either may be sequenced as PDX.

Patient is admitted with sepsis and meningitis. Treated with IV antibiotics for both conditions. Either may be sequenced as PDX.

2. Uncertain Diagnosis

"If the diagnosis documented at the time of discharge* is qualified as "probable," "suspected," "likely," "questionable," "possible," "still to be ruled out," or other similar terms indicating uncertainty, code the condition as if it existed or was established.

The bases for these guidelines are the diagnostic workup, arrangements for further workup or observation, and initial therapeutic approach that correspond most closely with the established diagnosis." OCG Section II.H.

Exception: Code only confirmed cases of HIV infection/illness and influenza due to certain viruses – H1N1, avian, novel influenza A.

Other terms qualified as uncertain diagnosis are "consistent with", "compatible with", "indicative of", "suggestive of", "comparable with", "appears to be". "Evidence of" does not qualify as uncertain diagnosis.

This guideline is applicable only to inpatient admissions (not outpatient visits).

Example: *"RLL pneumonia possibly due to aspiration." Code aspiration pneumonia.*

Many coding experts interpret "at the time of discharge" to imply documentation in the discharge summary or final progress note. However, the second sentence of this rule suggests that the* ***entire record* *should be considered when interpreting and applying this rule. The Official Coding Guidelines also state, "The entire record should be reviewed to determine the specific reason for the encounter and the conditions treated."*

The key issue is to ensure that the uncertain nature of a diagnosis or condition remains uncertain and is not further clarified at the time of discharge. For example, "possible gram-negative pneumonia" would not be assigned when later determined to be pneumococcal.

3. Codes for Symptoms, Signs, and Ill-Defined Conditions

"Codes for symptoms, signs, and ill-defined conditions from Chapter 16 are not to be used as principal diagnosis when a related definitive diagnosis has been established." OCG Section II.A.

Example: *Syncope due to cardiac arrhythmia. Cardiac arrhythmia is the PDX, syncope is secondary diagnosis.*

Do not assign a separate code at all for signs and symptoms that are routinely associated with a disease process.

Example: *Viral gastroenteritis with fever, abdominal pain, nausea, vomiting, diarrhea. Code only viral gastroenteritis.*

When applying this rule, remember that Rule #3 treats uncertain diagnoses as "established."

Example: *Fever possibly due to UTI. Code UTI only.*

See further details regarding coding of Signs & Symptoms in the section that follows.

Why Signs/Sx – Code dx first

4. Original Treatment Plan Not Carried Out

"Sequence as the principal diagnosis the condition, which after study occasioned the admission to the hospital, even though treatment may not have been carried out due to unforeseen circumstances." OCG Section II.F.

Example: *A patient with cholecystitis was admitted to the hospital for a cholecystectomy. Prior to surgery, the patient fell and sustained a left femur fracture. The surgery was canceled and a hip pinning was carried out on the second hospital day.*

The PDX remains cholecystitis, since it necessitated the admission to the hospital. The fractured femur is sequenced as a secondary diagnosis since it occurred during the hospital stay.

5. Complications of Surgery and Other Medical Care

"When the admission is for treatment of a complication resulting from surgery or other medical care, the complication code is sequenced as the principal diagnosis." OCG Section II.G.

The physician must indicate the condition is a "complication" or "due to" previous medical care/surgery in his or her documentation. A cause-and-effect relationship must be documented. The term "postop" by itself does not necessarily establish a cause-and-effect relationship.

Examples:

A patient was discharged two days following a hysterectomy. On the second day at home, she strained lifting a small child. She was readmitted with wound dehiscence. Sequence the wound dehiscence as the PDX.

A patient is admitted with respiratory failure and large iatrogenic pneumothorax 3 days following outpatient thoracentesis for malignant pleural effusion. Iatrogenic pneumothorax is the PDX.

6. Admission From Observation Units

Medical Observation: "When a patient is admitted to an observation unit for a medical condition, which either worsens or does not improve, and is subsequently admitted as an inpatient of the same hospital for this same medical condition, the principal dignosis would be the medical condition which led to the hospital admission." OCG Section II.I.1.

Postoperative Observation: "When a patient is admitted to a observation unit to monitor a condition (or complication) that developed following outpatient surgery, hospitals should apply the Uniform Hospital Discharge Data Set (UHHDS) definition of principal diagnosis as 'that condition established after study to be chiefly responsible for occasioning the admission of the patient to the hospital for care." OCG Section II.I.2.

Example: *A patient is treated in an observation unit for 16 hours with an exacerbation of COPD, then admitted as an inpatient for treatment of a pulmonary embolism discovered on chest CT. Pulmonary embolism is PDX.*

7. Admission From Outpatient Surgery

If admitted following an outpatient surgery due to a complication of the surgery, assign the complication as principal diagnosis. OCG Section II.J.

Example: *Patient admitted for postoperative bleeding following outpatient TURP; postoperative bleeding would be the PDX.*

If no complication or other condition is documented as the reason for admission, assign the reason for the surgery as PDX.

If admitted due to an unrelated condition, assign the unrelated condition as PDX.

8. Two or More Comparative/Contrasting Diagnoses

"In those rare instances when two or more contrasting or comparative diagnoses are documented as "either/or" (or similar terminology), they are sequenced according to the circumstances of the admission. If no further determination can be made as to which diagnosis should be principal, either diagnosis may be sequenced first." OCG Section II.D.

Example: *"Acute pancreatitis vs. acute cholecystitis": Either may be sequenced as PDX.*

9. Symptom Followed by Contrasting/ Comparative Diagnoses

"When a symptom(s) is followed by contrasting/comparative ["**or**"] diagnoses, the symptom is sequenced first. *However, if the symptom code is integral to the conditions listed, no code for the symptom is reported (ICD-10 change).* All the contrasting/ comparative diagnoses should be coded as additional diagnoses." OCG Section II.E.

Example: *Chest pain due to either angina* **or** *esophageal spasm. Chest pain is the PDX, with angina and esophageal spasm as additional diagnoses. (ICD-10: Chest pain would not be coded since chest pain is integral to these conditions).*

Example: *Syncope: Dehydration vs. cardiac arrhythmia. Syncope is the PDX, with dehydration and cardiac arrhythmia as secondary diagnoses.*

However, if a symptom is followed by two definitive ("**and**") diagnoses, then either condition can be sequenced as the principal diagnosis based on Rule #1.

Continued —

Example: *"Chest pain due to angina* ***and*** *esophageal spasm": Either angina or esophageal spasm may be PDX.*

Note: This rule does not apply to secondary diagnoses—assign the symptom only (see *Coding Clinic,* First Quarter 1998, p. 9)

Other important (chapter-specific) coding rules for assigning the principal diagnosis are included below. Specific coding rules are also included in Key References for the specific conditions listed in that section.

Diabetes

When a patient is admitted for a condition that is due to diabetes mellitus, the diabetes code 250.xx is assigned as the principal diagnosis, followed by the associated condition. OCG Section I.C.3.

Example: *A patient is admitted with a diabetic autonomic neuropathy. Sequence the diabetes code 250.6x as PDX, followed by autonomic neuropathy 337.1 as a secondary diagnosis.*

ICD-10: *Combination codes for diabetes will include the type of diabetes, body system affected, and the complications affecting that body system (category E08–E13). Sequencing is based on the reason for a particular encounter. Unspecified type defaults to Type 2. Diabetes documented as inadequately controlled, out of control, or poorly controlled are coded to diabetes, by type, with hyperglycemia.*

- *E10.40: Type 1 diabetes mellitus with diabetic neuropathy, unspecified*
- *E11.65: Type 2 diabetes mellitus with hyperglycemia*

Neoplasms

If the treatment is directed at the malignancy, designate the malignancy as the principal diagnosis. When a patient is admitted because of a primary neoplasm with metastasis and treatment is directed toward the metastasis only, the metastasis is designated as the principal diagnosis even though the primary malignancy is still present. OCG Section I.C.2.

When a primary neoplasm has been excised but still being treated, (chemotherapy, etc.), the malignancy should be coded. If previously excised or eradicated and no further treatment and no evidence of any remaining malignancy at the primary site, do not code the malignancy.

Signs and symptoms associated with an existing primary or secondary malignancy cannot be used to replace the malignancy as principal diagnosis, regardless of the number of admissions or encounters for treatment and care of the neoplasm.

Admit Solely for Chemotherapy/Radiation Therapy. If the patient is admitted solely for the purpose of receiving chemotherapy or radiotherapy, V58.11 or V58.0 are sequenced as PDX.

Complications. When the reason for admission is treatment of complications associated with the malignancy or adverse effects of chemotherapy, and the complication is the focus of treatment (not the malignancy) sequence the complication as the PDX.

Dehydration. When the admission is for management of dehydration due to the malignancy or the therapy, or a combination of both, and ONLY the dehydration is being treated (IV rehydration), the dehydration is the PDX, followed by the malignancy code(s).

Anemia. When the admission is for management of an anemia associated with the malignancy or due to chemo-/immuno-/radiotherapy, and the treatment is ONLY for anemia, the anemia is

Neoplasms, Continued

designated as the PDX, followed by the malignancy code(s). If treatment of the malignancy or other conditions is provided and a transfusion given, the anemia is coded as a SDX.

> **ICD-10:** *When the admission/encounter is for management of an anemia associated with the malignancy, and the treatment is only for anemia, the appropriate code for the malignancy is sequenced as the principal or first-listed diagnosis.*

Pain

Pain should not be used as PDX when the underlying definitive diagnosis has been established by the physician. OCG I.C.6.a.

When the reason for the admission/encounter is *pain control or pain management only*, a code from category 338 is used as the PDX.

If the encounter is for any other reason except pain control or pain management, and a definitive diagnosis has not been established, assign the code for the specific site of pain first, followed by the appropriate code from category 338.

Pain due to a device is coded as a complication.

Neoplasm-Related Pain (338.3): Code **338.3** is assigned to pain (whether acute or chronic) documented as being related to or associated with a malignancy.

This code would be assigned as PDX when the stated reason for the admission/encounter is documented as pain control or pain management only.

Example: *"Patient admitted for insertion of porta-cath for administration of narcotics to control refractory pain due to malignancy." Code first 338.3, followed by malignancy.*

Poisoning

When a patient is admitted due to poisoning (defined as a reaction to the improper use of a medication), the poisoning is sequenced first, followed by the manifestation. OCG Section I.C.17.e.

Poisoning includes wrong person, wrong dose, wrong substance, wrong route of administration, combination with alcohol, combination with OTC (without MD approval), overdose, and toxicity due to a non-medicinal chemical substance.

> Example: *A patient is admitted with a cocaine overdose producing seizures with cocaine dependence. Sequence cocaine overdose (968.5) as PDX, with seizures and cocaine dependence as secondary diagnoses.*

An **adverse effect,** in contrast to poisoning, is a reaction to a therapeutic substance correctly prescribed and properly administered. In these cases the manifestation is coded first, followed by the appropriate E code for the drug causing it (E930–E949). Adverse effects include allergic reaction, toxicity, synergistic reaction, side effect, or idiosyncratic reaction. Documentation of a drug toxicity, such as Digoxin toxicity, is coded as an adverse effect unless it is specifically documented that the drug was incorrectly prescribed or taken.

> **ICD-10:** *Poisonings and adverse effects of medication (categories T36–T50) are expanded combination codes that identify the substance; poisoning, adverse effect, or underdosing; intent; and initial encounter, subsequent encounter, or sequela. Sequencing rules are unchanged.*
>
> *Toxic effects of nontherapeutic substances are separately assigned to categories T51–T65 as combination codes for substance, intent, and encounter.*

SECONDARY DIAGNOSIS CODING RULES

Other diagnoses are defined as: "All conditions that coexist at the time of admission, that develop subsequently, or that affect the treatment received and/or the length of stay. Diagnoses that relate to an earlier episode which have **no bearing** on the current hospital stay are to be **excluded."** OCG Section III.

Other conditions (either present on admission or occurring during admission) that require:

- Clinical evaluation, or
- Therapeutic treatment, or
- Diagnostic procedures, or
- Increased nursing care/monitoring, or
- Extended length of stay

Secondary conditions which are documented but which do not meet 1 of these 5 requirements should not be coded. A review of Coding Clinic, Second Quarter 2000, pp. 20–21 indicates that chronic conditions are usually reported (coded) but should still meet at least one secondary diagnosis coding criteria.

"Chronic conditions such as, but not limited to, hypertension, congestive heart failure, asthma, emphysema, COPD, Parkinson's disease, and diabetes mellitus are reportable", but "need to meet the UHDDS definition of 'other [secondary] diagnoses' [as stated in the Official Coding Guidelines Section III]".

The CDS/coder needs to determine if the documented conditions are clinically significant and warrant code assignment. As an example, morbid obesity has been noted as "clinically significant" in *Coding Clinic* 2011; this condition may require "increased nursing care" at a minimum, not to mention complexity of care and high risk of medical/surgical complications. However, documentation of "CHF" on an anesthesia assessment, without any further indications of ongoing treatment, does not suggest clinical significance and thus the condition would not be coded.

Abnormal Findings: Lab, x-ray, EKG, pathology, and other diagnostic test results are not coded unless the provider documents their clinical significance in the medical record.

> Example: *"Patient with serum sodium of 125." Do not code unless physician states "hyponatremia."*

If the x-ray report provides additional information regarding the site for a condition that the provider has already diagnosed, it is appropriate to assign a code to identify the specificity that is documented in the x-ray report. *CC* 2013, Q1, p. 28.

Conditions From Previous Encounters: "Documentation from the current encounter should clearly reflect those diagnoses that are current and relevant for that encounter. It is inappropriate to go back to previous encounters to retrieve a diagnosis without **physician confirmation.**" *CC* 2013, Q3, p. 27. Therefore, it would be appropriate to query the physician regarding a condition from a previous encounter if it meets the definition of a secondary diagnosis for the current encounter (being treated, clinically evaluated, etc.)

The **Uncertain Diagnosis** rule also applies to the assignment of secondary diagnoses per OCG Section III.C.

Definition: A "sign" is objective evidence of disease observed by examining the patient, a "symptom" is a subjective observation reported by the patient. A "diagnosis" is a statement of conclusion that describes the reason for a disease, illness, or problem.

Misperceptions associated with the coding of signs and symptoms are a common source of coding errors. The coding guidelines discourage assigning codes for signs and symptoms, instead of a diagnosis.

General Guidelines:

"Codes that describe symptoms and signs as opposed to diagnoses are acceptable for reporting purposes when a related definitive diagnosis has not been established (confirmed) by the provider" (OCG, General Guidelines, Section I.B.6).

"Signs and symptoms that are associated routinely with a disease process should not be assigned as additional codes, unless otherwise instructed by the classification." (OCG, General Coding Guidelines, Section I.B.7)

"Additional signs and symptoms that may not be associated routinely with a disease process should be coded when present."

The determination of what signs and symptoms are "routinely associated with" every disease process encountered is one of the challenges coders face. This does not constitute "interpretation of the medical record", but does require coders to be familiar with the signs and symptoms of disease processes. To achieve this high standard, training in pathophysiology and medical terminology combined with continuing education and experience is absolutely essential.

Continued —

Principal Diagnosis Related Guidelines:

"Codes for symptoms, signs, and ill-defined conditions from Chapter 16 **are not to be used** as principal diagnosis when a related definitive diagnosis has been established." (OCG, Section II.A.)

"When a symptom(s) is followed by contrasting/comparative diagnoses, the symptom code is sequenced first. All the contrasting/comparative diagnoses should be coded as additional diagnoses." (OCG, Section II.E.)

"Symptoms, signs and ill-defined conditions in Chapter 16 characteristic of, or associated with a primary or secondary site malignancy cannot be used to replace the malignancy as the principal or first-listed diagnosis regardless of the number of counters for treatment and care of the neoplasm."

The instructional note at the beginning of Chapter 16 is specific about the limitations placed on the assignment of codes from categories 780–796. The situations in which it may be necessary to assign a sign or symptom code are:

- "No more specific diagnosis can be made even after all the facts bearing on the case have been investigated"
- "Provisional diagnoses in a patient who failed to return [for treatment]"
- The patient was "referred elsewhere … before the diagnosis was made"
- "A more precise diagnosis was not available for any other reason"
- "Signs or symptoms … that proved to be transient and whose cause could not be determined"
- "Certain symptoms which represent important problems in medical care and which it might be desired to classify in addition to a known cause"

For inpatients, codes are assigned to the highest degree of specificity **documented** by providers in the medical record, including uncertain diagnoses (those documented as probable, suspected, likely, etc.). According to CMS: "When sufficient clinical information isn't known or available about a particular health condition to assign a more specific code, it is acceptable to report the appropriate 'unspecified' code."

Therefore, when a documented diagnosis results in an unspecified code, a query is needed only when a more specific code impacts DRG assignment, quality outcomes, CMS pay for performance initiatives, or helps to justify medical necessity. Documentation of greater specificity by providers is not necessary simply because a more specific code exists.

The Official Guidelines, Section I.A.5.b, instructs coders to limit the use of unspecified codes as follows: "**Codes (usually a code with a 4th digit 9 or 5th digit 0 for diagnosis codes) titled 'unspecified' are for use when information in the medical record is insufficient to assign a more specific code.**"

Unspecified, or NOS, codes should not be assigned when more specific detail is documented in the medical record. The medical record should be searched carefully for any additional information that might permit assignment of a more specific code, thereby giving a more accurate and complete account of the patient's condition and treatment.

Two of the most commonly assigned unspecified codes are:

- Pneumonia, organism unspecified (486)
- Congestive heart failure, unspecified (428.0)

For pneumonia, if there is any documentation whatsoever by any provider that suggests the actual, probable, or suspected organism or other cause being treated, this ought to provide sufficient information to assign a more specific code. A positive culture result alone in the absence of provider documentation is not sufficient to assign a specific organism, but deserves a query for clarification (*Coding Clinic,* Second Quarter 1998, p. 3).

NOS (NOT OTHERWISE SPECIFIED)

The term "congestive heart failure" is considered nonspecific, outdated, and inadequate to describe this condition. Finding documentation of systolic and/or diastolic failure or dysfunction, and the acuity, anywhere at all in the medical record by a provider should permit assignment of the correct and most specific codes. If the necessary information isn't there, a query would be appropriate.

ICD-10:

Official Coding Guidelines, Section I.A.9.b: Codes titled "unspecified" are for use when the information in the medical record is insufficient to assign a more specific code. For those categories for which an unspecified code is not provided, the "other specified" code may represent both other and unspecified.

Section I.B.18: "Sign/symptom and "unspecified" codes have acceptable, even necessary, uses. While specific diagnosis codes should be reported when they are supported by the available medical record documentation and clinical knowledge of the patient's health condition, there are instances when signs/symptoms or unspecified codes are the best choices for accurately reflecting the healthcare encounter. Each healthcare encounter should be coded to the level of certainty known for that encounter."

ICD-9 and ICD-10 have a requirement, called the etiology/manifestation convention, for a few specific diagnoses that requires the underlying condition (cause/etiology) to be sequenced first followed by its manifestation (effect). It applies *only* to a limited number of diagnostic conditions and their manifestations as specifically identified by Tabular List instructional notes. The rule does not apply to codes for other conditions without these specific instructions.

Using an encoder/grouper greatly simplifies the process since the required condition-specific sequencing is incorporated in the encoder logic.

The Official Coding Guidelines, Section I.A.6., says it best: "Certain conditions [specified by the classification] have both an underlying etiology and multiple body system manifestations due to the underlying etiology. For such conditions, ICD-9-CM has a coding convention that requires the underlying condition be sequenced first followed by the manifestation. Wherever such a combination exists, there is a 'use additional code' note at the etiology code, and a 'code first' note at the manifestation code. These instructional notes indicate the proper sequencing order of the codes, etiology followed by manifestation."

Examples include: Diabetes mellitus; dementia; many infectious organisms including TB, syphilis, diphtheria; and liver cirrhosis (with esophageal varices)

Section I.A.6. goes on to explain: "In addition to the notes in the tabular [list], these conditions also have a specific index entry structure. In the index both conditions are listed together with the etiology code first followed by the manifestation codes in brackets. The code in brackets is always to be sequenced second.... 'Code first' and 'Use additional code' notes are also used as sequencing rules in the classification for certain codes that are not part of an etiology/manifestation combination [e.g., multiple coding for a single condition – see Section I.B.9.]."

Continued —

E/M Convention Does Not Apply to Other Conditions. Other than the conditions/codes specified by the ICD-9-CM classification, the etiology/manifestation convention ***does not apply*** to other diagnostic codes or conditions.

As stated in Section II.B.: When there are two or more interrelated conditions (such as diseases in the same ICD-9-CM chapter or manifestations characteristically associated with a certain disease) potentially meeting the definition of principal diagnosis, either condition may be sequenced first, unless the circumstances of the admission, the therapy provided, or the Alphabetic Index indicate otherwise.

For example, a diagnostic statement of "acute renal failure due to dehydration" does not require you to sequence dehydration (etiology) first, with acute renal failure (manifestation) as an additional diagnosis.

Of course, signs and symptoms of any condition might be considered "manifestations" of that condition. However, as discussed elsewhere, the signs and symptoms related to or associated routinely with an established or confirmed condition are not separately coded at all; therefore, there is no sequencing issue involved.

ICD-10: *No changes from the ICD-9 guidelines. E/M convention will no longer apply to diabetes due to the combination codes for this condition.*

Coding of complications of care (categories 996–999) is one of the most complex challenges faced by coders. Until recently there has been limited specific direction from ICD-9-CM Official Coding Guidelines. Commercial encoder logic can lead the most experienced coder astray.

Starting in 2011, the Guidelines and numerous *Coding Clinic*s have been particularly clear: *As with all procedural or postprocedural complications, code assignment is based on the provider's documentation of the relationship between the condition and the procedure. Not all conditions that occur during or following surgery are classified as complications. First, there must be more than a routinely expected condition or occurrence. In addition, there must be a cause-and-effect relationship between the care provided and the condition, and an indication in the documentation that it is a complication. The physician must explicitly document whether the condition is a complication.*

The following is an effort to provide a consistent approach to this complex task based on the available resources and our own professional experience and training.

General Guidelines

- No time limit is defined for the development of a complication of care. It may occur during the hospital episode in which the care was provided, shortly thereafter, or even years later!
- Remember that the most current version of ICD-9-CM and the Official Guidelines for Coding and Reporting always take precedence over any other source of coding advice.
- Whenever there is doubt, confusion, disagreement, or conflicting information about the correct interpretation of documentation in the medical record, the attending physician should be queried.

Continued —

Specific Guidelines

Not all conditions that occur during or following medical care or surgery are classified as complications. To properly code a condition as a complication of care, there must be:

1) An **unexpected or unusual outcome** caused by the care rendered—not a routinely expected or common condition or occurrence.

   For example, a significant amount of blood loss is usual and expected with joint replacement surgery; hemorrhage would not be considered a complication of care unless such bleeding is particularly excessive or unexpected.

   Physician documentation is very important and should be specific.

2) A **cause-and-effect relationship** between the care provided and the condition is established, and an indication in the documentation that it is a complication.

   Exception: In OB cases, the provider must specifically state that a condition is NOT affecting a pregnancy or it is assumed to be so.

Codes 996–999. The instructional note preceding categories 996–999 specifically excludes "complications of conditions for which the procedure was performed." This makes it extremely important to recognize the difference between a complication of care and a complication of the underlying condition being treated.

Continued —

Official Coding Guidelines. Section I.B.18 states: "Code assignment is based on the provider's documentation of the relationship between the condition and the care or the procedure."

Do not assume a cause-and-effect relationship exists. To be most specific, physicians should state that a particular condition is "due to" or "resulted from" or "the result of" a procedure or the care provided to identify it as a complication of care.

Encoder Issues. Don't become encoder-dependent. Terminology in the Index or Tabular List of ICD-9-CM can often provide insight or guidance. Also check Includes and Excludes notes carefully.

Implicit Conditions. In some cases, the causal relationship is implicit in the condition or the circumstances documented in the medical record or specified by the Index and Tabular List like:

- A complication due to the presence of an internal device, an implant or graft, or a transplant
- A cardiac complication occurring *during* surgery
- A postop wound infection complicating a simple appendectomy
- Wound dehiscence

Specific documentation of the term "iatrogenic" literally means "caused by a physician (i.e., medical care)."

ICD-10: *Complications of surgical and medical care (T80–T88) are very similar to ICD-9 but with greater specificity. Many complication codes are reassigned to specific chapters.*

Continued —

Postop Conditions. The term "postop" is particularly ambiguous and confusing; it literally means "occurring after surgery" and does not by itself necessarily establish a cause-and-effect connection. It is so problematic that even the Arkansas Foundation for Medical Care (AFMC) has specifically advised physicians: "If a patient has a condition that occurred in the post-operative period, but it is not considered a complication of the procedure, the term "postop" should not be used."

Most postop conditions cannot be coded as a complication of care unless explicitly specified by the physician as a complication. Specific examples include:

- Postop cardiac arrhythmia (assign 997.1 only if physician states the condition is a complication: *Coding Clinic*, First Quarter 1994, p. 20)
- Postop CVA (documentation should clearly specify the cause-and-effect relationship between the medical intervention and the CVA in order to assign this code [997.02]: Official Coding Guidelines I.C.7.c)
- Postop hemorrhage (Code 998.11 is assigned only when the physician specifically documents the blood loss, anemia, or hemorrhage was a complication of the procedure: *Coding Clinic*, Second Quarter 1992, p. 15; First Quarter 2011, p. 13)
- Postop infection occurring after a heavily contaminated orthopedic injury or preoperatively infected surgical field (complication of the condition for which the procedure was performed)

References: Coding Clinic, *Third Quarter 2009, p. 5, and First Quarter 2011 pp. 13–14; and Official Coding Guidelines, Section I.B.18.*

AFMC, "Physician Documentation and Inpatient Prospective Payment System (IPPS) Reimbursement," January 2008.

A present on admission (POA) indicator must be reported for all principal and secondary diagnoses and external cause of injury codes. This is required to identify complications of care.

The **POA indicators** are:

Y (Yes): Present at the time of inpatient admission

N (No): Not present at the time of inpatient admission

U (Unknown): Documentation is insufficient to determine if condition is present on admission (MD should be queried)

W (Clinically undetermined): Provider is unable to clinically determine whether condition was present on admission or not

1 (Unreported/not used): Exempt from POA reporting

A POA indicator of U (unknown) is equivalent to N (no), and W (clinically undetermined) is equivalent to Y (yes).

POA Definition: Present at the time the order for inpatient admission occurs. Conditions that develop during an outpatient encounter, including emergency department, observation, or outpatient surgery, are considered as present on admission.

POA Documentation. Medical record documentation from any provider involved in the care and treatment of the patient may be used to support the determination of whether a condition was present on admission. The term "provider" means a physician or any qualified healthcare practitioner who is legally accountable for establishing the patient's diagnosis.

CMS has no limitation on the time period during which a provider must identify or document that a condition was present on admission.

Continued —

PRESENT ON ADMISSION (POA)

Conditions That Are Present on Admission Are Defined As:

- Any condition the provider explicitly documents as present at the time of admission.

- Conditions that were diagnosed prior to admission.

- Conditions diagnosed during the admission that were clearly present but not diagnosed until after admission occurred.

- Diagnoses subsequently confirmed after admission if at the time of admission they are documented as suspected, possible, rule out, differential diagnosis, or constitute an underlying cause of a symptom that is present at the time of admission.

- A final diagnosis that contains a possible, probable, suspected, or rule out diagnosis, and this diagnosis was based on symptoms or clinical findings suspected at the time of inpatient admission.

- All parts of a combination code were present on admission.

  Examples:
  - Patient with diabetic nephropathy admitted with uncontrolled diabetes
  - Patient admitted with ruptured aortic aneurysm

- Any E code representing an external cause of injury or poisoning that occurred prior to inpatient admission.

  Example: Patient fell out of bed at home.

Reference: Official Coding Guidelines, Appendix I: Present on Admission Reporting Guidelines.

Any Healthcare "Provider." Documentation in the medical record by any healthcare provider is appropriate for code assignment.

The term **"provider"** includes physicians and "any qualified health care practitioner who is legally accountable for establishing the patient's diagnosis" such as consultants, residents, nurse practitioners, physician assistants, etc.

Exception: Code assignment for the BMI, pressure ulcer stage codes, and depth of non-pressure chronic ulcers (new for ICD-10) may be based on medical record documentation from clinicians (e.g. nursing) who are not the patient's provider.

Attending vs. Consulting Physician. Code assignment may be based on other physician (i.e., consultants, residents, anesthesiologists, etc.) documentation as long as there is no **conflicting** information from the attending physician. Medical record documentation from any physician involved in the care and treatment of the patient, including documentation by consulting physicians, is appropriate for the basis of code assignment.

A physician query is not necessary if a physician involved in the care and treatment of the patient has documented a diagnosis and there is no conflicting documentation from another physician.

If documentation from different physicians conflicts, seek clarification from the **attending** physician, as he or she is ultimately responsible for the final diagnosis.

It is important to distinguish between "conflicting" and "more specific." For example, pneumonia vs. bronchitis is conflicting and would require a query; pneumonia vs. aspiration pneumonia is more specific and would not.

Continued —

Code From the Entire Record: According to the Official Coding Guidelines, p. 1, "The entire record should be reviewed to determine the specific reason for the encounter and the conditions treated."

When documentation in the medical record is clear and consistent, coders may assign and report codes. Documentation is not limited to the face sheet, discharge summary, progress notes, history and physical, or other report designed to capture diagnostic information. This advice refers only to inpatient coding (*Coding Clinic,* Second Quarter 2000, p. 17).

Clinical Validation

CMS does not permit providers to submit claims with codes that cannot be validated or substantiated by the clinical findings, criteria, or circumstances documented in the record. If "clinically invalid" diagnoses are coded on claims that result in improper payments, there can be serious consequences for the hospital. This is one of the principal activities of the RAC program and other auditors.

The days of "coding whatever the doctor documents" without clinical validity are gone. This responsibility falls squarely on the coder's shoulders, and together with the professional ethical standards, now requires coders to have the training and experience to recognize and confirm validating clinical criteria and circumstances.

Collaboration between coders and documentation specialists can provide a powerful resource for meeting this responsibility.

References:

Coding Clinic, *Second Quarter 2000, p. 17.*
Coding Clinic, *First Quarter 2004, p. 18.*
CMS MLN Matters *SE1121.*

INTRODUCTION TO CODING AND DRGS

Coding describes the process used to transform disease, injury, and procedure descriptions into alpha-numeric codes. The aggregation of clinical data into reportable categories supports requirements ranging from reimbursement to statistical analysis of diseases and therapeutic actions to public health surveillance.

Uniform Hospital Discharge Data Set (UHDDS). The UHDDS definitions are used by acute care hospitals to report codes and other inpatient data elements on the hospital billing claim in a consistent manner. These definitions stipulate the types and numbers of diagnoses and procedures which are reported on the claim.

- All diagnoses that affect the current hospital stay are to be reported. The claim form will permit a reporting of up to 25 diagnoses, including the admitting diagnosis.
- All significant procedures are to be reported. Up to 25 procedure codes can be submitted on the claim.

Inpatient Prospective Payment System (IPPS). In 1983 the IPPS system was introduced by the federal agency now known as the Centers for Medicare & Medicaid Services (CMS) as a means to curb skyrocketing healthcare costs for Medicare patients. Under IPPS, the codes assigned to documented diagnoses and procedures in patient medical records also assign each patient to one of several hundred categories, known as "Diagnosis Related Groups" (DRGs).

The assigned DRG is associated with a pre-determined, fixed payment rate used to reimburse the hospital for services provided to the patient. The objective of IPPS was to change hospital behavior through financial incentives that encourage more cost-efficient management of medical care. As frequently happens with initiatives implemented by CMS, other payers began to adopt DRG methodologies as a reimbursement mechanism.

Continued —

Diagnosis Related Groups (DRGs). DRG systems are inpatient classification schemes that categorize patients who share similar clinical characteristics and costs. Each inpatient discharge is classified into a DRG based on the ICD-9-CM coded data submitted on the hospital billing claim. Multiple DRG systems exist; examples include:

- Medicare Severity DRGs (MS-DRGS) – used by Medicare
- All Patient Refined DRGs (APR-DRGs) – used by many Medicaid programs
- AP-DRGs – All Patient DRGs – used by some payers

The DRG payment for a hospital inpatient is determined by multiplying the relative weight for the DRG by the hospital's blended rate. As an example:

MS-DRG 293 – Heart Failure	
Relative Weight (RW)	0.6723
Hospital Blended Rate	$5,500
= MS-DRG Payment	$3,698
Geometric Length of Stay (GMLOS)	2.7

The **RW** is indicative of length of stay, severity of illness, and resource utilization and reflects the relative cost for treating patients during the prior year. A higher RW suggests a "sicker," more resource intensive patient.

The **Hospital Blended Rate** is the total dollar amount assigned to a hospital to calculate MS-DRG reimbursement and includes a base rate plus add-ons for local wage variations, teaching hospitals, and hospitals with a disproportionate share of indigent patients. The blended rate is unique to each hospital and is updated each year by CMS to reflect inflation, technical adjustments, and budgetary constraints.

The **GMLOS** is the national mean length of stay for the MS-DRG. By excluding outlier cases, the geometric mean reduces the effect of very high or low values, which might bias the mean if a straight average (arithmetic mean) is used. The GMLOS is used to determine the per diem payment rate for patients transferred to a post-acute care setting for specified MS-DRGs. For example, if a patient is transferred to another acute care hospital before the GMLOS is reached, the hospital is paid twice the per diem rate for the first day of the stay, and the per diem rate for each subsequent day up to the full MS-DRG amount.

Case Mix Index. A hospital's case mix index (CMI) is the average of the DRG weights for a specific patient volume and time period. The CMI indicates the average weight or severity of a patient population. A low CMI may denote DRG assignments that do not adequately reflect the severity of illness, the resources used to treat a patient, or the quality of care provided. A CMI calculation example follows:

Population: Traditional Medicare Inpatient Acute Time Period: January to June 2013				
DRG	DRG Description	RW	DC Volume	Total RW
470	Major Joint Replacement	2.1463	286	613.8418
871	Sepsis with MCC	1.8527	243	450.2061
291	CHF with MCC	1.5031	126	189.3906
378	GI Hemorrhage with CC	1.0029	193	193.5597
683	Renal Failure with CC	0.9655	80	77.2400
Sum			928	1524.2381
CMI (Total RW / DC Volume)				1.6425
Reimbursement [Discharge Volume x CMI] x Blended Rate ($5,500)				$8,383,320

To illustrate the impact of documentation and coding on reimbursement:

> A 25% reduction in the MCC capture rate for MS-DRG 871 (Sepsis) in the above example would negatively impact the CMI by 0.0515 resulting in a reimbursement loss of approximately $263,000 for this six month period.

External Audits. Due to the impact of code assignment on MS-DRGs and hospital reimbursement, CMS (and other payers) frequently audit medical records to determine if the hospital was paid appropriately. If audits indicate that codes were assigned without supporting documentation and/or were not in accordance with coding guidelines, the hospital may be denied all/some of the provided reimbursement.

Ethical Standards. The American Health Information Management Association (AHIMA) has published standards for ethical coding for coding professionals. The Association of Clinical Documentation Improvement Specialists (ACDIS) also has a published a Code of Ethics. These standards prohibit misrepresenting the patient's clinical picture through coding to inappropriately increase reimbursement, justify medical necessity, improve publicly reported data, or qualify for insurance policy coverage benefits.

MS-DRG Fundamentals

MS-DRG Assignment. MS-DRG assignment is driven by the following:

- Principal diagnosis
- Secondary diagnoses
- Procedures
- Gender
- Discharge status

Principal Diagnosis. Correctly identifying the principal diagnosis is the most important factor in DRG assignment. The principal diagnosis code is the first code listed on the hospital claim and is defined as "that condition established after study to be chiefly responsible for occasioning the admission of the patient to the hospital for care."

Secondary Diagnoses. All other conditions, either present on admission or that develop subsequently, may qualify as secondary diagnoses if they affect patient care. CMS has designated certain of these conditions as CCs (comorbidities or complications) and MCCs (major CCs) that may affect DRG assignment.

- Comorbidity. A preexisting condition that because of its presence with a specific diagnosis causes an increase in the length of stay by at least one day in approximately 75% of cases.

- Complication. A condition that arises during the hospital stay that prolongs the length of stay by at least one day in approximately 75% of the cases.

- Complication/Comorbidity (CC). A condition defined by CMS in the MS-DRG system that contributes significantly to the severity of illness and complexity of care of patients. The presence of even a single CC often enhances the relative weight of most DRGs.

- Major CC (MCC). A condition defined by CMS in the MS-DRG system that contributes to substantially greater severity of illness and complexity of care than simple CCs. The presence of even a single MCC dramatically enhances the R.W. of most MS-DRGs.

Continued —

Not a CC	CC	MCC
"Altered mental status"	Acute Delirium	Metabolic or Toxic Encephalopathy
End-Stage Lung Disease on Home O2	Chronic Respiratory Failure	Acute on Chronic Respiratory Failure
Cystitis	UTI Bacteremia	Septicemia or Sepsis due to UTI
Angina or CAD	Unstable Angina CAD of CABG graft	Non-ST segment elevation MI
CHF	Systolic CHF Diastolic CHF	Acute Systolic CHF Acute Diastolic CHF

A diagnosis designated as an MCC or CC may be excluded from impacting the MS-DRG. Such CMS defined exclusions occur when the MCC or CC is too closely related to the principal diagnosis. For example, CKD stage 5 is a CC, however when used with a principal diagnosis of acute renal failure the CC is excluded from impacting the MS-DRG; it does not "count".

An example of the impact of the accurate capture of the principal and secondary diagnoses:

Pneumonia MS-DRGs		
"HCAP"	"Pneumonia due to Aspiration"	"Sepsis due to Pneumonia"
195 w/o CC 0.6997 194 w CC 0.9771 193 w MC 1.4550	179 w/o CC 0.9741 178 w CC 1.3955 177 w MCC 1.9934	871 w MCC 1.827

Continued —

Procedures. All significant procedures are to be reported. UHDDS defines significant procedures as those that are surgical in nature; carry a procedural risk; carry an anesthetic risk; or require specialized training.

An example of the impact of the accurate capture of procedures:

Skin Ulcer DRGs			
With Debridement		With Excisional Debridement	
594 w/o CC	0.6814	572 w/o CC	1.0077
593 w CC	1.0094	571 w CC	1.4906
592 w MCC	1.4131	570 w MCC	2.4154

Discharge Status. The UHDDS defines values required on claims to report the patient's discharge disposition, e.g., home, AMA, transferred, expired. When the discharge disposition code indicates the patient was discharged with continuing healthcare services (e.g., acute care hospital transfer, skilled nursing facility admission, home health services) the hospital's MS-DRG reimbursement may be reduced.

As an example, a patient with an acute MI who expires will be assigned to MS-DRG 283 instead of 280. Discharge status can also impact MS-DRG reimbursement for post-acute care transfers.

Coding Fundamentals

In hospitals, codes are assigned by individuals ("coders") with extensive training in anatomy, pathophysiology, and coding classification systems.

After each patient's discharge, a review of the patient's entire medical record is performed to identify and assign codes to all reportable conditions documented by physicians in the patient record.

The ICD-9-CM (soon to be ICD-10-CM and ICD-10-PCS) coding classification system is used to provide the assigned codes. These classification systems are accompanied by guidelines which regulate the assignment process to promote consistent and compliant code assignment. The conditions and procedures coded must be documented by the physician and clinically supported by information contained in the medical record. For example, if the hospital bills a diagnosis code for pneumonia, physician documentation must include a diagnosis of pneumonia, and the clinical information and treatment provided must also substantiate a diagnosis of pneumonia.

The codes are submitted on claims to payers for reimbursement and aggregated by various entities, including CMS, to support comparative outcome analyses.

Coding Classification Systems. Since 1978, the ICD-9-CM system has been the official coding classification system used to assign codes to diagnoses and procedures associated with hospitalization in the United States. In October 2014 ICD-9-CM will be replaced with ICD-10-CM for the reporting of diseases and conditions, and with ICD-10-PCS (Procedure Coding System) for hospital reporting of inpatient procedures. ICD-10-CM is a vast improvement over the 30-year-old ICD-9, with a more logical organization and standardized, consistent codes and definitions. The greatest improvement in ICD-10-CM is that it allows for much greater coding specificity, laterality, and ease of expansion.

Continued —

Diagnosis Code Structure. ICD-9-CM diagnosis codes are 3 to 5 digits, while those for ICD-10-CM are 3 to 7 characters long and are alphanumeric. Codes are to be used and reported at the highest number of characters available based on physician documentation.

An example of a diagnosis code for Cerebral Infarction (CVA):

ICD-9-CM Diagnosis Code Structure					
4	3	4	•	9	1

ICD-10-CM Diagnosis Code Structure							
I	6	3	•	5	0		
Category				Etiology Anatomic site Severity			Extension

Diagnosis Code Selection. An Alphabetic Index (alphabetical list of terms and their corresponding codes) is used to look up codes for diagnoses and procedures documented in the medical record. These codes are then reviewed in the Tabular List, a structured list of codes in numerical order divided into chapters based on body system or condition.

Both the Index and Tabular List must be used together to assign the correct code. Software programs, called "encoders" and/or "groupers" simplify and support the code assignment process.

Procedure Code Structure. ICD-9-CM medical and surgical procedure codes are 3 or 4 digits, while those for ICD-10-PCS are always 7 alphanumeric characters.

Continued —

An example of a procedure code for lysis of peritoneal adhesions:

ICD-9-CM Procedure Code Structure				
5	4	•	5	9

ICD-10-PCS Procedure Code Structure						
0	**D**	**N**	**W**	**0**	**Z**	**Z**
Section	**Body System**	**Root Operation**	**Body Part**	**Approach**	**Device**	**Qualifier**
All codes in PCS are 7 characters. Characters are alphanumeric: letters O and I are not used since they can be confused with numbers 0 and 1. Each character has a meaning. Meanings change by Section. Sections provide the first character. The "placeholder" Z is used for characters when there is no value (when not applicable), such as no device.						

Procedure Code Selection: ICD-9-CM procedure codes are accessed in the same manner used for diagnosis codes; an Alphabetic Index is used to identify codes which are subsequently looked up in the Tabular List for additional instructions.

ICD-10-PCS introduces significant changes to procedure code selection and assignment. In ICD-10-PCS, codes are constructed using individual values from Tables. An Alphabetic Index exists to locate the appropriate root operation Table, but is not required.

- Tables are grouped by Sections. Sections identify the general type of procedure (e.g., Medical and Surgical, Obstetrics, Imaging), Body System, and Root Operation. Inpatient discharges primarily require use of the Medical and Surgical Section ("0").

Continued —

- Values exist in the tables for each of the PCS characters 4-7; these values are used to construct the code. All values must come from the same row.

- A code refers to all 7 characters. Few unspecified options exist.

- Appendices in the *ICD-10-PCS Reference Manual* may be a helpful resource, e.g., Body Party Key, Device Key.

Code Updates. ICD-9-CM, soon to be ICD-10-CM and ICD-10-PCS, is updated each year by the "Cooperating Parties" which consist of the American Health Information Management Association (AHIMA), National Center for Health Statistics (NCHS), Centers for Medicare and Medicaid Services (CMS), and the American Hospital Association (AHA).

Coding Guidelines. Coding guidelines exist to promote accurate, consistent code assignment. Three authoritative sources of coding guidelines exist and are listed in order of hierarchy:

1) ICD-9-CM (ICD-10-CM) Classification Guidelines: Contained within the ICD Classification System in the Alphabetic Index and/or Tabular List.

2) Official Guidelines for Coding and Reporting (updated annually): Set of rules that have been developed to accompany and complement the official conventions and instructions provided within the ICD system itself.

3) AHA *Coding Clinic* publications (distributed quarterly): Provide clarification on application of the guidelines.

The hospital can develop its own supplemental guidelines if they do not conflict with those set forth in the authoritative coding guideline sources (*Coding Clinic*, First Quarter 2000, p. 24).

MS-DRG Payments. The transition to ICD-10-CM was designed by CMS to have as little impact on hospital payment as possible. Studies using general equivalence mappings (GEMs) and native coding have so far demonstrated this to be the case. A 3M impact analysis of the ICD-10 conversion project on Medicare MS-DRG payments to hospitals confirmed a slight overall hospital payment decrease of 0.04 percent ($4 per $10,000). These limited effects are intrinsic to the ICD-10 classification system and not subject to changes in physician documentation.

Coding Guidelines. Apart from the new codes, most of the Official Coding Guidelines for ICD-10-CM remain the same. The MCC/CC lists and DRG assignments were highly correlated and preserved. A few notable changes include the coding of acute MI, pathologic fractures, open fractures, CAD and angina, and sequencing of anemia when due to malignancy.

CDI Program Activities. The purpose of an effective CDI program is to ensure compliant documentation and correct coding of diagnoses and procedures that affect:

- MS-DRG and/or APR-DRG assignment,
- Quality/performance profiles, and
- Prompt submission of claims.

The scope of such efforts includes education; effective queries for physician clarification; systematic, focused program processes; and open communication among all stakeholders.

Specificity of Codes. The ICD-10 classification is intended to provide codes that can precisely and completely express what the physician documents (regardless of his/her specificity). It is not intended to establish a standard of specificity to which the physician must conform.

Continued —

To provide greater diagnostic specificity of ICD-9 or ICD-10 codes that are required to support correct MS-DRG assignment and accurate quality/performance profiles, queries will be necessary. If there is no DRG or quality/performance impact, greater specificity isn't necessary, and queries are not needed.

Query Frequency. ICD-10-CM is expected to have little impact on the types and frequency of necessary queries. Although ICD-10-CM codes generally include more detail than ICD-9-CM codes, unspecified or default codes still exist for all diagnoses. What remains unclear is how payers will respond to ICD-10 code specificity (or to what extent quality/performance profiles will be affected) in the future as ICD-10 data is gathered and analyzed.

If and when any such changes occur in the future, providers will have advance notice and can adjust accordingly. CMS has already stated that no changes to MS-DRGs will be made based on ICD-10 for at least two years.

ICD-10-PCS does not provide unspecified codes. An increase in query volume might occur for procedures in the unlikely event that the documentation necessary for assigning a code is not available, but ICD-10 procedural gap analyses have shown few documentation gaps. Unlike ICD-9, documentation from other parts of the record, such as diagnostic radiology reports, will be used to assign the necessary specificity.

Increased Post-Discharge CDS and Coder Collaboration. The complexity of ICD-10-PCS will likely increase the need for post-discharge collaboration between coders and CDS. While CDS concurrent review will typically focus on procedures needed for accurate working MS-DRG assignment, the coder will be required to assign PCS codes for all significant procedures. Coders may find clinical assistance from the CDS helpful for accurate code assignment.

Continued —

Productivity. Studies of coder productivity indicate that the transition to ICD-10 will cause a significant reduction in coder productivity at the outset, because of both the need to learn the new coding classification system and the time it will take to identify sources of documentation required for code assignment, primarily related to ICD-10-PCS.

With sufficient training and accumulating experience, however, it is expected that staff will regain or even surpass their earlier ICD-9 productivity levels. The transition to ICD-10 should reduce the practice of assigning excessive and irrelevant diagnostic and procedural codes (such as certain V-codes, transfusions, etc.), which should ultimately increase coding process efficiency.

ICD-10-CM Coding Rules and Guideline Changes

Most of the guidelines are exactly the same between ICD-9-CM and ICD-10-CM. The General Coding Guidelines and Conventions including the format of the Index and Tabular list, abbreviations and punctuation (NEC, NOS, brackets, colons), Includes notes, and steps in assigning codes are all the same.

ICD-10-CM provides a clearer definition for **Excludes** notes:

- An Excludes1 note indicates that a coder should never use the code excluded with the code above the Excludes1 note. The two conditions cannot occur together.

- An Excludes2 note means the condition is not included in the code. It indicates that the condition excluded is not part of the condition represented by the code, and a patient may have both conditions at the same time. When an Excludes2 note appears under a code, coders may report both the code and the excluded code together when appropriate.

Continued —

Defaults in ICD-10-CM include:

If not specified as ...	Then the default is ...
Open or closed fracture	Closed
Displaced or not displaced fracture	Displaced
Hemiplegia – Affected side is specified but not if dominant	Right side: Dominant Left side: Non-dominant Ambidextrous:Dominant
Gustilo Type (for certain open fractures)	Open Fracture I/II (B)
Type I or II Diabetes	Type II
Postop pain acute/chronic	Acute

Some of the more notable differences are in the Chapter Specific Guidelines of the Official Coding Guidelines and include:

- **Anemia associated with neoplasm:** Admission for anemia associated with malignancy and treatment is only for the anemia, code for malignancy is sequenced first. If anemia associated with chemotherapy, immunotherapy or radiation therapy and treatment only for anemia, anemia is coded first.

- **Diabetes:** Combination codes for DM (instead of two codes) that include type of diabetes, body system affected with complications affecting that body system. "With hyperglycemia" is coded when stated as inadequately controlled, out of control, poorly controlled.

- **Hypertension:** No distinction between benign, malignant, unspecified.

Continued —

- **Acute MI:** Acute MI (code I21x) is used if within 4 weeks and continued treatment. Subsequent acute MI (code I22x) is coded when another MI occurs within 4 weeks of the first MI. Code I21x is always coded in conjunction with a subsequent MI. Sequencing depends on the circumstances of the admission.

- **Injuries:** A 7th character is used to designate the encounter as initial, subsequent, or sequelae.

  A fracture in a patient with known osteoporosis is assumed to be pathologic unless the nature of the injury would be expected to fracture a normal, healthy bone. A code from category M80 Osteoporosis with current pathologic fracture is used.

  Certain open fractures are further specified by Gustilo fracture classification I/II (wounds with up to moderate soft tissue damage) or III (high-energy wounds with extensive soft tissue damage). The default 7th character B for open fracture type I/II is assigned if the Gustilo fracture type is not specified.

Background

Pay for Performance (P4P) programs are intended to reward hospitals for providing high quality care or improving the quality of care they provide to patients, or penalize them for substandard care. The Affordable Care Act contains provisions for three separate programs that are part of this long-standing effort by CMS to link healthcare quality to Medicare payments:

- Hospital Value Based Purchasing Program (HVBP)
- Hospital Readmission Reduction Program (HRRP)
- Hospital-Acquired Condition (HAC) Reduction Program.

Hospital Value Based Purchasing (HVBP)

Each year Medicare will withhold an increasing percentage of hospital DRG payments to fund HVBP reaching a total of 2% by October 1, 2016. High achieving hospitals will be rewarded with incentive payments from these funds based on how well they perform compared with other hospitals. Hospitals with lower performance will be penalized since 2% of their Medicare revenue will have been withheld.

HVBP is designed to promote better clinical outcomes for hospital patients, encourge cost reduction, and improve patient experience of care during hospital stays. It consists of four components (domains) all of which are also reported on the CMS Hospital Compare website:

1) Clinical Process of Care - 13 measures selected from preexisting core measures (12 in FY2015)
2) Outcome – 3 measures (5 in FY2015)
3) Patient Experience of Care – 8 measures from the national patient survey
4) Efficiency – Medicare spending per beneficiary (FY2015)

The current outcome measures are risk and severity-adjusted and include 30 day mortality rates for acute MI, heart failure, and pneumonia. For FY2015, the Efficiency measure and two new Outcome measures are added: AHQR Composite Patient Safety Indicator #90 and the CLABSI (central line-associated blood stream infection) rate.

Hospital Readmission Reduction Program (HRRP)

HRRP imposes a monetary penalty on hospitals for excess readmissions of Medicare patients 65 years of age or older with the diagnoses of acute MI, heart failure, or pneumonia. The maximum penalty for the current FY 2014 is 2% and will be 3% each year thereafter. For FY 2015 (starting October 1, 2014), two additional diagnoses will be added: COPD and elective hip or knee replacement.

A readmission is defined as a patient who is readmitted to the same or another acute care hospital within 30 days of discharge. Certain readmissions are exempt such as "planned" chemotherapy or rehabilitation.

Excess readmission rate is defined as exceeding the risk-adjusted national mean readmission rate. This means that at least 50 percent of hospitals will face some penalty every year. In the first year of HRRP (October 1, 2012-September 30, 2013) about 70 percent of hospitals were penalized an aggregate total of $280 million.

Hospitals are also required to report data for hospital-wide, all-cause readmission rates for all patients (not just Medicare patients), which are reported on the CMS Hospital Compare website.

Hospital-Acquired Condition (HAC) Reduction Program

CMS has designated certain conditions that it considers "preventable" as "hospital acquired conditions" when they were not present on admission (occurring during hospitalization). HACS are identified by Medicare when the POA (present on admission) indicator assigned on the hospital claim form is "N" (not present on admission) or "U" (insufficient documentation).

The importance of documenting or clarifying the POA status of such conditions to avoid improper classification as a HAC cannot be over-emphasized.

Beginning in FY 2015 (October 1, 2014), Medicare will penalize hospitals that perform poorly for certain selected HACs. Under the HAC Reduction Program, hospitals with a risk-adjusted ranking in the lowest-performing quartile (lowest one-fourth) for these HACs will be **penalized 1%** of their total Medicare DRG payments. This HAC reduction program is separate from, and does not replace, the pre-existing HAC non-payment program.

These targeted HACs are classified in 2 categories (domains):

1) AHQR Patient Safety Indicator (PSI) 90 weighted 35%:

- Pressure ulcer – Stage 3 and 4 (or unstageable)
- Iatrogenic pneumothorax
- Central venous catheter-related blood stream infection
- Post-op hip fracture
- Perioperative pulmonary embolism or DVT
- Post-op sepsis
- Post-op wound dehiscence
- Accidental puncture or laceration

2) Two CDC National Health Safety Network measures weighted 65%:

- CLABSI (central line associated blood stream infection)
- CAUTI (catheter-associated UTI)

Risk Adjustment: Secondary Diagnoses

The HVBP outcome measures, HRRP readmission rates and HAC reduction ranking are risk-adjusted. Various risk adjustment methodologies are used and consider factors such as age, gender, and multiple comorbid conditions (secondary diagnoses). Documentation and coding of such conditions is crucial to ensure that these outcome measures and readmission rates are accurately reflective of the hospital's risk-adjusted performance.

HAC Non-Payment Program of the Deficit Reduction Act

Since October 1, 2008, Medicare has not assigned an inpatient hospital discharge to a higher-paying DRG when a HAC was coded as a secondary diagnosis, excluding them as MCC or CC. CMS reasoned that hospitals should not receive higher reimbursement based solely on the occurrence of a "preventable" condition while hospitalized. If another MCC/CC is present, the claim will be paid at the higher DRG rate based upon those diagnoses. The 14 current non-payment HACs are:

1. Foreign object retained after surgery
2. Air embolism
3. ABO blood incompatibility
4. Pressure (decubitus) ulcers—Stages III & IV
5. Iatrogenic pneumothorax with venous catheterization
6. Falls/trauma occurring after admission
7. Catheter-associated UTI
8. Vascular catheter-associated infection
9. Manifestations of poor glycemic control
10. Surgical site infection, mediastinitis, following CABG
11. Surgical site infection following certain orthopedic procedures (spine, neck, shoulder, elbow)
12. Surgical site infection following implantable cardiac electronic devices
13. Surgical site infection following bariatric surgery for obesity
14. DVT and PE following total knee replacements and hip replacements

Medicare DRGs are used primarily for patients over age 65. To better accommodate the entire patient population, both adult and pediatric, 3M and the National Association of Children's Hospitals and Related Institutions (NACHRI) collaborated in 1990 to develop the 3M APR-DRG system.

APR-DRG is a proprietary, severity-adjusted system often used for quality assessment programs, such as the Agency for Health Research and Quality (AHRQ), and many state database performance reporting systems. Eleven states have adopted APR-DRGs for inpatient payment by either Medicaid or Blue Cross, and more states are slated to follow suit.

APR-DRGs are similar in structure to MS-DRGs, with generally comparable base DRGs split into severity levels based on secondary diagnoses. Each base APR-DRG has 4 levels of severity of illness (SOI) and 4 levels of risk of mortality (ROM), as opposed to up to 3 severity levels for MS-DRGs using MCCs and CCs (see Table 1 below). Consequently, there are more APR-DRGs than MS-DRGs (1,262 vs. 746).

Table 1

MS-DRG	**APR-DRG**
Main Driver: Principal Diagnosis or Surgical Procedure	Main Driver: Principal Diagnosis or Surgical Procedure
Secondary Diagnosis: • MCC • CC • Non-CC	Secondary Diagnosis: • SOI 4 (Extreme) • SOI 3 (Major) • SOI 2 (Moderate) • SOI 1 (Minor)

APR-DRG Assignment: Assignment of APR-DRGs is highly complex; statistical algorithms and rerouting logic were used to determine the final DRG and severity level. By comparison, MS-DRGs are straightforward, intuitive, and transparent.

Continued —

APR-DRG OVERVIEW

The APR-DRG system assigns discharges to a DRG SOI subclass as follows:

1) Assign Base DRG by principal diagnosis and principal procedure
2) Determine the severity of illness (SOI) level for each secondary diagnosis
3) Assign the final DRG/SOI subclass based on the combination and hierarchy of all diagnoses

Table 2: Example of APR-DRG 45

Base DRG	SOI	DRG Description
45	1	CVA & Precerebral Occlusion w/ Infarct
45	2	CVA & Precerebral Occlusion w/ Infarct
45	3	CVA & Precerebral Occlusion w/ Infarct
45	4	CVA & Precerebral Occlusion w/ Infarct

The more common MS-DRG MCCs are classified in APR-DRG as SOI Level 3 or 4, CCs are SOI 2 or 3, and most non-CCs are SOI 1. A few non-CCs are assigned as SOI 2.

While a single MCC or CC determines the MS-DRG, multiple secondary diagnoses can influence the APR-DRG. Not all secondary diagnoses make a difference in the final APR-DRG assignment, however: in most circumstances, only two or three secondary diagnoses with the highest SOI levels are needed to determine the final APR-DRG SOI level.

Continued —

Determining Severity of Illness Using MS-DRGs

While a single MCC or CC determines the MS-DRG assignment, one or two more may alter the severity of illness (SOI) classification as measured by the APR-DRG system. Submitting queries for every possible MCC/CC without knowing the effect on SOI is ineffectual, inefficient, and an unnecessary burden on busy physicians.

Knowing which additional MCCs or CCs could affect a particular case would allow the CDS to focus only on those that are pertinent to SOI. However, not all coders and CDS have access to the APR-DRG grouper to identify SOI level and the documentation opportunities affecting SOI.

As an alternative, the CDS needs a strategy to optimize severity classification working only with MCCs and CCs in the MS-DRG system:

1. Using the SOI level of the most common and important MCC/CCs identified in the MCC/CC section of this guide, the CDS can determine the likely APR-DRG SOI in most cases (see Table 3).
2. Alternatively (see Table 4), obtaining a combination of 2 or 3 MCC/CCs will usually result in a reasonable SOI classification.

With experience, the CDS can learn to combine both strategies. While imperfect, the result will usually be a solid SOI classification in the absence of the APR-DRG grouper. In addition, documentation and coding of 2 MCC or CCs guards against RAC DRG changes, since RACs often focus on cases with only one MCC or CC.

Continued —

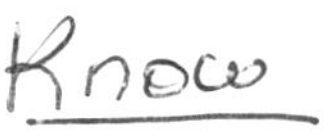

Table 3: APR-DRG SOI Levels

Combination of Secondary Diagnosis SOI	APR-DRG SOI Level*
Two SOI 4, or One SOI 4 and two SOI 3	4 (Extreme)
Two SOI 3, or One SOI 3 and two SOI 2	3 (Major)
One or more SOI 2	2 (Moderate)

*APR rerouting logic, exclusions, and patient age may result in a different SOI level.

Table 4: Severity Impact Using MCC/CCs

Strategy	Description
Two MCCs	If only one MCC is identified and clinical indicators of another MCC are present, query the physician for this second MCC.
One MCC + Two CCs	If only one MCC is identified and there are no clinical indicators for a second MCC, search and query for up to two additional CCs.
Two CCs	If there are no clinical indicators for any MCC, search and query for up to 2 CCs.

With the emergence of value based purchasing, pay for performance and growing emphasis on severity-adjusted quality of care, the accuracy of coded healthcare data has become more important than ever before. One of the most valuable tools for ensuring data accuracy is an effective and compliant physician query process.

The Official Coding Guidelines describes this interaction as follows: "A joint effort between the health care provider and the coding professional [or documentation specialist] is essential to achieve complete and accurate documentation, code assignment, and reporting of diagnoses and procedures."

CMS has recognized the appropriateness of physician queries but cautions that they should not be leading in nature and should not introduce new information not otherwise contained in the medical record.[1]

However, CMS has deferred the promulgation of specific guidelines addressing these practices to health information management experts and organizations. CMS allows the use of the physician query to the extent it provides clarification and is consistent with other medical record documentation.[1]

Four professional guidelines establishing an industry standard for query/clarification practices have been published:

1. 2001 AHIMA Practice Brief: Developing a Physician Query Process, Journal of AHIMA 72: 88 I-M.
2. 2008 AHIMA Practice Brief: Managing an Effective Query Process, Journal of AHIMA 79: 83-88, which replaced the 2001 Practice Brief.
3. 2010 AHIMA Practice Brief: Guidance for Clinical Documentation Improvement Programs, Journal of AHIMA 81, which supplemented but did not replace the 2008 Practice Brief.

4. 2013 AHIMA/ACDIS Query Guidance, which supplemented but did not replace previous advice.

All professionals involved in the query process should adhere to these guidelines regardless of credentials, position, or title.

Definition of Query

A query is a communication tool used to clarify documentation in the health record for accurate code assignment. It is a question posed to a provider to obtain additional, clarifying information to improve the specificity and completeness of the data used to assign diagnosis and procedure codes.

Reasons for a Query

The query process has become a common communication and educational method to advocate proper documentation practices and ensure data accuracy and integrity. Queries may be made for the following situations:

- Clinical indicators of a diagnosis but no documentation of the condition
- Clinical evidence for a higher degree of specificity or severity
- A cause-and-effect relationship between two conditions or organism
- An underlying cause when admitted with symptoms
- Only treatment is documented (without a diagnosis)
- Present on admission (POA) indicator status

Whom to Query?

Any physician or other qualified healthcare practitioner who is legally accountable for establishing a patient's diagnosis.

Attending physician
Emergency physician
Intern, resident, fellow
Podiatrist

Consultants, specialists
Anesthesiologist, CRNA
Physician assistant
Nurse practitioner

The provider must be licensed by his or her state
tialed by the facility to diagnose and treat patients.

When there is conflicting information, the attending physician should be queried since he or she is ultimately responsible for the final diagnoses.

When to Query?

Query when there is **conflicting, incomplete, or ambiguous** information in the health record regarding a significant reportable condition or procedure. According to the OCG: "The importance of **consistent, complete documentation** in the medical record cannot be overemphasized."

AHIMA/ACDIS 2013 recommends queries when documentation:

- Is conflicting, imprecise, incomplete, illegible, ambiguous, or inconsistent
- Describes or is associated with clinical indicators without a definitive relationship to an underlying diagnosis
- Includes clinical indicators, diagnostic evaluation, and/or treatment not related to a specific condition or procedure
- Provides a diagnosis without underlying clinical validation
- Is unclear for present on admission indicator assignment

Queries are essential to provide greater diagnostic specificity for codes that are required to support correct DRG assignment and for accurate quality/performance profiles. Otherwise, queries really have no other utility. If there is no DRG, quality, or performance impact, greater specificity isn't necessary.

AHIMA 2008 states: "Queries are not necessary for every discrepancy or unaddressed issue in physician documentation … Entities must balance the value of collecting marginal data against the administrative burden of obtaining additional documentation."

The Medicare Program Integrity Manual, Section 6.5.3.B regarding DRG validation states:

"Contractors [reviewers] shall ensure that the hospital reports the principal diagnosis and all relevant secondary diagnoses on the claim. **The relevant diagnoses are those that affect DRG assignment."**

When Not to Query

Codes assigned to clinical data should be clearly and consistently supported by provider documentation. *Coding Clinic* Second Quarter 2000, p. 17: "When documentation in the medical record is clear and consistent, coders may assign and report codes."

Queries should not be used to question a provider's clinical judgment, but rather to clarify documentation. In situations where the clinical information or clinical picture does not appear to support the documentation of a condition or procedure, hospital policies should provide guidance on a process for addressing the issue.

Documentation of Query Response

A query response can be documented in the progress notes, discharge summary, addendum, or on the query form as a part of the formal health record. An addendum should include actual date of entry and authentication.

Query types include:

Concurrent
- Initiated by clinical documentation specialist (CDS)
- Real-time while still in hospital and under care
- More timely, accurate, and reliable
- May improve quality of care
- Verbal or written

Retrospective (post-discharge)
- Initiated by coder
- Concurrent query did not occur
- After discharge, before claim submission
- Clarify documentation for accurate coding
- Must be retained as permanent part of medical record if provider answers on the query form itself

Post-Bill
- After claims submission or after payment
- Initiated by authorized personnel pursuant to routine billing/business office policies
- Usually result of payer inquiry or determination, audits or other internal monitor, or to support an appeal
- Written only / retained as permanent part of medical record

Written Queries should:
- Identify the relevant clinical indicators/information from the medical record/episode of care that is the basis of the query and show why a more complete or accurate diagnosis or procedure is requested
- Ask the provider to make a clinical interpretation of these facts based on professional judgment
- Not appear to lead the provider to document a particular response
- Not sound presumptive, directing, prodding, probing, or as though the provider is being led to make an assumption

Multiple-Choice Queries, where applicable, have advantages over open-ended queries. They can be clear, precise, and specific helping the provider understand the purpose and give a reasoned clinical response. AHIMA/ACDIS 2013 provides guidance for the proper construction of multiple-choice queries:

- "Multiple choice query formats should include **clinically significant and reasonable options** as supported by clinical indicators in the health record." Non-CC/MCC options are not required unless they are "clinically significant and reasonable" for the circumstances.

- "Providing a new diagnosis as an option in a multiple choice list – as supported and substantiated by referenced clinical indicators from the health record – is not introducing new information." Do not include new diagnoses/undocumented conditions among the indicators supporting the query.

- Multiple-choice query formats should include additional options such as: other, clinically undetermined, not applicable.

Verbal Queries are a common component of the concurrent query process that allows for an information/educational exchange between CDS and provider. They should be conducted in a manner consistent with written query guidelines.

A summary of the verbal query should be recorded in CDS working documents with:
- Clinical indicators that support the query,
- The nature of question posed to the practitioner in general terms (not verbatim), and
- Time and date of the discussion.

Leading or Non-Leading

A leading query is one that is not supported by the clinical elements in the health record and/or directs a provider to a specific diagnosis or procedure. AHIMA/ACDIS 2013 offers the following advice:

"The simplest way to ensure that queries remain non-leading is to include evidence from the medical record and provide the opportunity for the treating physician to offer additional input through the use of multiple response options."

Examples of Leading Queries:

Dr. Smith – Based on your documentation, this patient has anemia and was transfused 2 units of blood. Also, there was a 10 point drop in hematocrit following surgery. Please document "acute blood loss anemia," as this patient clearly meets the clinical criteria for this diagnosis.

Dr. Jones – This patient has COPD and is on oxygen every night at home and has been on continuous oxygen since admission. Please document "chronic respiratory failure."

Examples of Non-Leading Queries:

Dr. Smith – In your progress note on 6/20, you documented anemia and ordered transfusion of 2 units of blood. Also, according to the lab work done on 11/26, the patient had a 10 point drop in hematocrit following surgery. Based on these indications, please document, in the discharge summary, the type of anemia you were treating.

Dr. Jones – This patient has COPD and is on oxygen every night at home and has been on continuous oxygen since admission. Based on these indications, please indicate if you were treating one of the following diagnoses:

- Chronic respiratory failure
- Acute respiratory failure
- Acute on chronic respiratory failure
- Hypoxia only
- Unable to determine
- Other

Yes/No Query

The AHIMA/ACDIS 2013 guideline expanded the proper use of "yes/no" queries which include:

- Substantiating or further specifying a diagnosis that is already present in the health record

  Example: Metabolic encephalopathy is documented in the record only once on 7/22 and not listed in the discharge summary. Did this patient actually have metabolic encephalopathy?

- Establishing a cause-and-effect relationship between documented conditions such as manifestation/etiology, complications and conditions/diagnostic findings

  Example: The patient was admitted with TIA. Carotid Doppler shows 35 % stenosis of the right ICA. Was the TIA related to carotid stenosis?

- Resolving conflicting practitioner documentation

  Example: The pulmonologist diagnosed pneumonia in two progress notes. The discharge summary indicates bronchitis. Did this patient have pneumonia or bronchitis or both?

- Confirming present on admission status

  Yes/No queries should include an option for "other", "unable to determine", or "not clinically significant."

  Yes/No queries should not be used when only clinical indicators of a condition are present and the condition/diagnosis has yet to be documented. Multiple-choice or open-ended queries are preferred.

Query Retention

Organizational policies should specifically address query retention consistent with statutory or regulatory guidelines. The policy should indicate whether the query is part of the patient's permanent health record or stored as a separate business record. If the query form is not part of the health record, the policy should specify where it will be filed and the length of time it will be retained.

Although recommended by many experts, incorporating queries into the legal medical record may have undesirable consequences such as unnecessarily focusing attention on a missed diagnosis or a surgeon's reluctance to confirm a significant procedural complication.

Information From Prior Episodes of Care

Opinions and advice about the use of information from prior episodes of care for queries is confused and conflicting. Section III of OCG regarding the UHDDS definition of Other Diagnoses is widely referenced but misunderstood:

> "Diagnoses that relate to an earlier episode which have **no bearing** on the current hospital stay are to be excluded."

The OCG does not exclude information from earlier episodes of care that **do have a bearing** on the current hospital stay. *

Likewise, *Coding Clinic,* Third Quarter 2013, p. 27 recently affirmed this guideline as follows:

> "Documentation for the current encounter should clearly reflect those diagnoses that are current and relevant for that encounter [including those from prior encounters]... The physician is responsible for diagnosing and documenting all relevant conditions... [If] the recurring condition is still valid for the outpatient encounter or inpatient admission,

Continued —

> the recurring condition should be documented in the medical record with each encounter/admission. However, if the condition is not documented in the current health record, it would be inappropriate to go back to previous encounters to retrieve a diagnosis [for code assignment] **without physician confirmation**."

While coders should not assign codes for conditions not documented in the current record, the query process is a proper method for obtaining the necessary physician confirmation of recurring/chronic diagnoses from prior episodes of care that may still be valid for, pertinent to, or have a bearing on the current encounter. It remains the physician's responsibility to decide. Clinical data from a prior episode to support the query should be included in the current episode of care.

As an example, OCG requires that if AIDS has ever been previously diagnosed, code 042 must be assigned on every subsequent encounter. If only HIV or HIV-positive is documented for the current episode of care for a patient with AIDS, clarification that the patient has AIDS must be obtained for correct assignment of code 042.

Standardized Query Templates

"Standardized" clarification/query templates for the most common physician queries have many advantages over free-text queries:

- Uniform, consistent content and structure
- Greater clarity, detail, and specificity of information submitted to physicians, especially with multiple-choice format
- Less time and effort composing the queries, resulting in greater efficiency
- Minimal training requirements for effective use; less dependence on composition skills

Continued —

- Consistency between concurrent and retrospective (post-discharge) queries
- Assurance of compliance with AHIMA standards and recommendations
- Assurance of compliant standards through multidisciplinary vetting and approval of queries and incorporation into facility CDI policy

Audit Contractors

Audit contractors and other reviewers may request copies of physician queries, which must be provided when they are retained as a part of the legal medical record. CMS recommends that providers make available all relevant information (whether from the medical record or other administrative documents) that supports coding and DRG assignment. Each facility should develop consistent and compliant query retention and release policies.

(1) CMS Policy Clarification on Coding Compliance, QIP TOPS Control Number: PRO2001-13, dated October 11, 2001.

Leukemia:

- Has specific digit that indicates "in remission"
- If completely cured → assign hx V-code

Lymphoma:

- No specific digit for "in remission" so "current," "code 2," assigned when in remission
- if completely cured → V code

dx:
V45.11 Renal dialysis Status
(Adm. for other reason, but gets dialysis)

39.95 Hemodialysis (procedure)

TABLE OF CONTENTS

ACUTE BLOOD LOSS ANEMIA

Definition of Anemia

The technical definition of anemia is "decreased red blood cell mass" which is difficult to measure. As a practical matter anemia is defined as a hemoglobin/hematocrit level below normal reference range for the lab performing the test. The World Health Organization (WHO) defines anemia using hemoglobin levels as follows:

- Men < 13.0 gm/dl
- Women < 12.0 gm/dl
- Pregnancy < 11.0 gm/dl

As a general rule of thumb, one gm/dl of hemoglobin is usually equivalent to a hematocrit of 3%. For example, hemoglobin of 13 gm/dl corresponds to a hematocrit of 39%.

Definition of Blood Loss Anemia: Anemia due to loss of blood.

The key concept to focus on is "anemia"; loss of enough blood to become anemic or more anemic for patients with preexisting chronic anemia. Documentation by the physician of anemia due to blood loss is definitive – not the amount of blood lost or whether a transfusion was given.

What if the patient was anemic to start with and became more anemic? How much of a drop in hemoglobin/hematocrit is significant enough to warrant a diagnosis of blood loss anemia? Several criteria may be useful:

- Transfusion given
- Development of symptoms of anemia not previously present
- Drop in hemoglobin of 1.0–2.0 gm/dl and/or hematocrit of 3–6% (a smaller drop is more significant with a lower baseline)

It may be useful to develop a guideline defining acute blood loss anemia in these patients taking into consideration the above criteria.

Blood loss that is excessive or unusual may suggest a diagnosis of "hemorrhage" that represents a complication of care (code 998.11), but must be specified as a complication by the physician to be assigned as 998.11. If unclear, the attending physician should be queried. See *Coding Clinic* 1992 Q2 P15, and 2011 Q1 P13.

Coding: The ICD-9-CM Classification Index indicates that:

Anemia due to:	Code
Acute blood loss Acute hemorrhagic Acute post-hemorrhagic Postop blood loss, acute or unspecified	285.1 (CC)
Chronic (or unspecified) blood loss Chronic (or unspecified) hemorrhagic Chronic (or unspecified) post-hemorrhagic Chronic post-op blood loss	280.0
Post-op (not specified as blood loss)	285.9
Hemorrhage, post-operative hemorrhage, or unusual / excessive blood loss *specified as a complication*	285.1, 998.11 (CC)

Sequencing of Anemia Due to GI Bleeding: When patients are admitted for acute GI bleeding, it is nearly always sequenced as the principal diagnosis and the acute blood loss anemia as a secondary diagnosis (CC).

Sometimes patients are admitted for chronic blood loss anemia due to chronic GI bleeding (known or unknown cause) and transfused. If there is no evaluation, treatment or management directed at the chronic GI bleeding, the anemia is typically sequenced as principal diagnosis. The chronic GI bleeding (and its cause, if known) would be a secondary diagnosis.

If however, the admission does involve evaluation or treatment of the GI bleed or its cause, then these conditions may be sequenced as principal diagnosis based on the circumstances of the admission.

ICD-10: *One code for anemia specified as acute blood loss, acute post-hemorrhagic, or post-procedural due to blood loss (D62).*

Reference:

WHO: "Haemoglobin concentrations for the diagnosis of anaemia and assessment of severity".

Acute renal failure same acute renal injury (AK

Definition: Sudden reduction of kidney function, usually within a period of hours or days. AKI may progress rapidly to permanent loss of renal function and requires immediate attention.

The terms acute renal failure and acute kidney injury (AKI) are synonymous for clinical and coding purposes. Attempts to reach agreed-upon criteria defining AKI (RIFLE 2004; AKIN 2007) had failed and remained controversial.

Finally, in March 2012, a National Kidney Foundation (NKF) conference (KDIGO[1]) established the first authoritative, widely accepted professional consensus definition of acute kidney injury (AKI).

KDIGO Clinical Criteria define AKI as any one of the following:

- Increase creatinine ≥ **0.3 mg/dl from baseline within 48 hours**; or
- Increase in creatinine level to ≥ **1.5x baseline**, which is known or *presumed* to have occurred within the prior 7 days; or
- Urine output < 0.5 ml/kg/hr for 6 hours

When baseline creatinine is unknown, KDIGO advises:

"The lowest SCr [creatinine level] obtained during a hospitalization is usually equal to or greater than the baseline. This SCr should be used to diagnose (and stage) AKI."

Time Frames for AKI: Even though the KDIGO criteria identify specific time frames for the occurrence of AKI, it clearly allows for clinical judgment in establishing the diagnosis:

"As with any clinical criteria, the timeframe for AKI is somewhat arbitrary… 'How far back can a baseline value be retrieved and still expected to be valid ...' In general, it is reasonable in patients without CKD [with previously normal renal function] to assume that SCr [creatinine level] will be stable over several months or even years, so that a SCr obtained 6 months or even 1 year previously would reasonably reflect the patient's pre-morbid baseline."

The 0.3 mg/dl criterion can only be applied prospectively when the baseline has been measured within the preceding 48 hours. The 1.5 times baseline criterion can be used retrospectively and prospectively with broad interpretation as discussed above.

Examples:

- A patient admitted with creatinine of 1.2 has an increase to 1.6 within 36 hours following IVP. This is AKI based on an increase creatinine from baseline of 0.4 (> 0.3) mg/dl in less than 48 hours.
- Creatinine on admission is 2.0 and decreases to 1.0 with IV fluids. This is AKI since the baseline is considered 1.0 and the admission creatinine was greater than 1.5 times the baseline.
- A patient with no known kidney disease is admitted with dehydration and a creatinine of 1.8 with a previous level of 1.0 six months ago. This is AKI: admission creatinine of 1.8 is greater than 1.5 times the "baseline" of 1.0.

Causes of AKI

The most common cause of AKI is dehydration (sometimes described as "prerenal"). However, with appropriate treatment including prompt IV hydration, it is often reversible.

Other causes are classified as:

- Renal, including numerous intrinsic pathologic processes such as acute tubular necrosis (ATN), acute papillary necrosis, glomerulonephritis, which are often associated with NSAIDs
- Post-renal due to obstruction of ureters or bladder

Acute Tubular Necrosis (ATN)

The two major causes of AKI in hospitalized patients are "pre-renal" AKI and acute tubular necrosis (ATN). ATN may be responsible for about one-third or more of inpatient acute renal failure.

Pre-renal AKI is due to reduced blood flow to the kidney caused by such things as dehydration, intravascular volume depletion (including diuretic-induced), edematous states (like cirrhosis or severe CHF), and hypotension. If not corrected promptly, pre-renal AKI may progress to ATN.

ATN is usually associated with hypotension, especially when severe, and when related to sepsis, surgery, and obstetrical complications.

IV contrast induced AKI is always due to ATN. Rhabdomyolysis with myoglobinuria also causes ATN. ATN can be caused by a variety of other drugs (i.e., NSAIDs) and toxins.

The hallmark of ATN that distinguishes it from simple "pre-renal" AKI is the response to fluid administration and rehydration. With ATN, it usually takes **more than 72 hours** for renal function to return toward baseline.

If additional urine testing is ordered, urinary sodium concentration > 40 meq/L and fractional excretion of sodium (FENa) > 2% support the diagnosis of ATN. However, with contrast-induced ATN the FENa may be < 2%.

Other less common causes of acute renal failure that qualify as MCCs are acute cortical necrosis and acute medullary (papillary) necrosis.

ACUTE KIDNEY INJURY

Coding and Documentation

The terms acute renal failure (ARF) and acute kidney injury (AKI) are synonymous for clinical and coding purposes. Code 584.9 encompasses both AKI and ARF. It is a CC, and can be used as a principal diagnosis.

A diagnosis of "[acute] renal insufficiency" is vague, non-specific, and does not reflect the severity associated with AKI. Also, documentation of "pre-renal azotemia" to describe AKI is non-specific and will result in assignment of an incorrect code.

For inpatients, AKI is frequently caused by acute tubular necrosis (ATN). Whenever findings suggest ATN, it should be clarified since ATN is a more specific diagnosis and classified for severity purposes as an MCC. "Toxic nephropathy" and "vasomotor nephropathy" are also terms for ATN and coded as ATN (code 584.5).

The BUN should not be used as an indicator of AKI since it can be elevated for many other reasons. When dehydration occurs without renal failure, the BUN will be elevated but the creatinine will remain at baseline.

Coding rules require that AKI be "coded first" when it is due to dehydration even if the only treatment is IV hydration (*Coding Clinic*, Third Quarter 2002, p. 21).

ICD-10: *No significant changes (category N17).*

[1]*Kidney Disease: Improving Global Outcomes (KDIGO) Acute Kidney Injury Work Group. KDIGO Clinical Practice Guideline for Acute Kidney Injury. Kidney Inter., Suppl. 2012; 2: 1–138.*

CHRONIC KIDNEY DISEASE (CKD)

Definition: A persistent and usually progressive, irreversible loss of kidney function, as measured by glomerular filtration rate (GFR). CKD is often associated with several common medical conditions: diabetes, hypertension, urinary obstruction, auto-immune diseases, multiple recurrent urinary tract infections, and any episode(s) of prior acute renal failure.

In addition, certain medications can cause renal damage that may progress to CKD, such as aspirin, acetaminophen (Tylenol), and NSAIDs (non-steroidal anti-inflammatory drugs) like ibuprofen, naproxen, indomethacin, ketoprofen, Celebrex, Toradol, and others.

Clinical practice guidelines for chronic kidney disease published by the National Kidney Foundation (NKF) identify five stages of CKD based on the GFR, followed by ESRD.

The GFR is proportional to the **stable baseline** creatinine level, but also depends on age, race, and gender. Laboratory reports of creatinine values typically provide the corresponding calculated GFR. For the NKF GFR calculator, see *www.kidney.org/professionals/kdoqi/gfr_calculator.cfm.*

Documentation Issues: Ideally, for accurate data collection, it is desirable for stage to be specified in all cases of CKD. It is essential that physicians document stage 4 and 5, since these represent CCs potentially affecting the severity classification and DRGs reported. Stages 1–3 and unspecified stage are not CCs.

Chronic renal insufficiency, chronic renal failure or chronic renal disease are equivalent to CKD but almost must be staged.

See table on next page.

CKD determination

Continued—

Stage CKD determination – GFR consistent for 90 days or more

CHRONIC KIDNEY DISEASE (CKD)

CKD Stage	GFR	Code	Approx. Serum Creatinine*
Stage 1	≥ 90	585.1	*< 0.9*
Stage 2	60-89	585.2	*1.0-1.3*
Stage 3	30-59	585.3	*1.4-2.4*
Stage 4 (CC)	15-29	585.4	*2.5-4.5*
Stage 5 (CC)	< 15	585.5	*> 4.5*
ESRD (MCC)	N/A	585.6	*Need for dialysis*
CKD, CRF, CRI (unspecified stage)	Unspecified	585.9	*N/A*

Stage 1 = Renal abnormality with normal GFR.

ESRD = Dialysis-dependent Stage 5.

*Elderly patients may have a higher CKD stage with lower creatinine than indicated here.

ICD-10: *No changes (category N18). Stage 1–5 (N18.1–N18.5), ESRD (N18.6), CKD unspecified (N18.9).*

ESRD comes in c̄ "SOB, volume overload" → code "volume overload" or maybe look for Pulmonary Edema

Definition: Brain infarction or hemorrhage usually associated with permanent or temporary neurologic deficits; includes transient focal neurologic deficits lasting longer than 24 hours.

Diagnostic Indicators:

Clinical indicators should be easily identified:

- Positive MRI or CT showing acute infarction or hemorrhage, or
- Persistent focal neurologic defect (> 24 hrs)

Physicians sometimes need to be reminded that persistence of a focal neurologic deficit > 24 hours from onset is a stroke (CVA), not a TIA. Duration is counted from onset, not presentation. Many patients present to the ER having had several hours or more of symptoms.

MRI without contrast, if available, is probably the best test to evaluate acute CVA (infarction or hemorrhage); CT is a second choice used mainly to rule out hemorrhage. Non-hemorrhagic CVA may not be visible on CT during the first 24 hours, and may not become evident for several days.

CVA vs. TIA:

TIA (Transient Ischemic Attack) is a brief period of focal neurologic deficit lasting **less than 24 hours (usually less than one hour)** due to temporarily blocked blood flow to a specific area of the brain.

Clinical Indicators of TIA:

- Symptoms resolve within 24 hours (usually less than 1 hour)
- No acute infarction or hemorrhage on CT / MRI

KR *See also TIA and Precerebral Occlusions or Embolism*

Tissue Plasminogen Activator (TPA)

While usually obvious in the medical record, remember to look for use of thrombolytic agent (DRG 61–63): tissue plasminogen activator (TPA). Patients presenting with symptoms of an acute cerebrovascular infarction who receive treatment with TPA are considered to have had a cerebral infarction. In these circumstances, *Coding Clinic* indicates that code 434.91 (cerebral artery occlusion with infarction) should be assigned.

If TPA infusion is started at another facility, TPA code 99.10 would not be coded by the receiving facility. TPA code 99.10 is only coded if started in the ED or hospital. If TPA infusion is started in another facility within 24 hours of transfer to current facility, assign code V45.88 (status post administration of TPA in a different facility within last 24 hours) whether or not the infusion is continued in the receiving facility.

ICD-10: *No significant changes except the hemorrhage or infarction can be specified to affected artery with laterality (category I60–I63).*

References: The Lancet 369: 293–298, 2007.
Coding Clinic, Third Quarter 2007, p. 12; First Quarter 2007, p. 23.

Clinical Definition: While there are no authoritative or consensus definitions, **acute** encephalopathy can be accurately described as an acute (or subacute) **generalized alteration** in all aspects of brain function (communication, memory, speech, orientation, behavior) due to a **systemic underlying cause** that is usually **reversible** resolves when the underlying cause is corrected.

Common causes of acute encephalopathy include fever, infection of any type, dehydration, electrolyte imbalance, acidosis, organ failure, sepsis, hypoxia, drugs, poisons, or toxins.

Acute encephalopathy is due to a reversible **functional** abnormality of the brain; so, imaging studies like CT and MRI are expected to be unremarkable. It should be distinguished from the chronic encephalopathies which are associated with permanent structural changes in the brain.

Classification of encephalopathy as acute or chronic is used for clarification of the functional and structural distinction between them, and is not required for diagnostic or coding specificity.

Some examples of the many chronic encephalopathies include: Korsakoff (alcohol), Binswanger (subcortical vascular dementia), traumatic, spongioform (viral), chronic toxic (cumulative exposure to solvents or heavy metals), and various hereditary metabolic disorders.

Specific Types of Acute Encephalopathy

- **Metabolic** (348.31) is intended to describe encephalopathy due to such things as fever, dehydration, electrolyte imbalance, acidosis, hypoxia, infection, and organ failure.

- **Toxic** (349.82) generally refers to the effects of drugs, toxins, poisons, and medications. Physicians may use this term clinically to describe encephalopathy caused by fever, sepsis, or other "toxic" conditions. When this occurs, no E-code will be assigned for a drug effect or toxicity.

- **Toxic-metabolic** (349.82) encephalopathy suggests a combination of toxic and/or metabolic factors. Physicians often use this term when only metabolic factors are present. Since the same code is used as for "toxic", there will be no E-code assigned unless a specific drug or toxin is also identified.

- **Septic** encephalopathy is a clinical term that expresses brain dysfunction as a manifestation of severe sepsis, and is coded 348.31 (metabolic).

- **Hepatic** encephalopathy is another specific clinical type assigned code 572.2 (MCC).

- **Unspecified** encephalopathy is coded 348.30.

Hypoxic or anoxic encephalopathy (brain damage) is assigned code 348.1 (CC), and codes for hypoxic ischemic encephalopathy (HIE) apply only to neonates. Dialysis-associated encephalopathy is coded as 293.9 or 294.8 (both non-CC/MCC).

Documentation Issues

The recognition of acute encephalopathy is crucial for accurate diagnostic and severity of illness classification. For many admissions, the principal reason for admission is actually the altered mental status due to underlying encephalopathy. In other cases it will be a serious comorbid condition. If not correctly documented with greater specificity as encephalopathy, altered mental status will be assigned as a minor symptom or not coded at all.

Ex UTI

Encephalopathy is assigned as the principal diagnosis if it is the primary reason for inpatient admission. For example, patients with a UTI are often admitted mainly for encephalopathy (mental status alteration), not for the UTI itself. Uncomplicated UTIs can usually be treated as outpatient or in observation; acute encephalopathy is a serious medical condition requiring inpatient care.

As a comorbid secondary diagnosis, the presence of an acute encephalopathy of almost any type (toxic, metabolic, septic, uremic, hepatic, even unspecified) qualifies as an MCC. Anoxic/hypoxic, alcoholic, and hypertensive encephalopathies are CCs.

Be alert for the **over-diagnosis** of "altered mental status" when not fully supported by the entire medical record—for example, nursing notes that do not confirm altered mental status or conflicting physician documentation. In such cases, a query for clarification is warranted, citing the conflicts in the record.

Dementia vs. Encephalopathy

A common clinical and coding problem is establishing and validating the diagnosis of encephalopathy when a patient with preexisting dementia is admitted with an altered mental status. This may represent simply a progression of dementia or alternatively encephalopathy imposed on baseline dementia.

This distinction should be relatively simple. A dementia patient has encephalopathy when:

- There is a genuine acute or subacute mental status alteration,
- Associated with metabolic or toxic factors, that
- Improves or returns to baseline status when the causative factors are corrected.

If no toxic or metabolic factors are evident, or if the patient's mental status does not improve during hospitalization, encephalopathy is unlikely.

ENCEPHALOPATHY

Delirium vs. Encephalopathy

The terms delirium and encephalopathy mean essentially the same thing clinically. However, from a coding perspective delirium (CC) is classified as a mental disorder or as a symptom; encephalopathy (MCC) is recognized as a serious, specific diagnostic condition that identifies toxic and metabolic states acutely affecting the brain.

Psychiatrists are often perplexed by this situation because the Diagnostic and Statistical Manual of Mental Disorders (DSM-5 released May 2013) definition of "delirium" is virtually identical to the clinical criteria for acute encephalopathy.

The typical features associated primarily with, and expected for, "delirium" (sometimes, but not always, associated with encephalopathy) are those of agitation, delusions, hallucinations, disorientation, or aberrant behavior.

For precise clinical documentation and correct coding, the diagnostic term encephalopathy is preferred for describing mental status alteration when due to toxic or metabolic causes. The term delirium is best reserved for psychiatric conditions unrelated to underlying systemic conditions.

> **ICD-10:** *No significant changes. Toxic encephalopathy (G92), metabolic or septic (G93.41), encephalopathy NEC (G93.49), or unspecified encephalopathy (G93.40) are MCCs.*

Excisional Debridement (86.22)

Surgical removal or **cutting away** of devitalized tissue, necrosis, or slough down to viable tissue using a **blade/scalpel** (not scissors). Can be performed in OR, ED, minor procedure area, or bedside. The use of the terms "sharp" or debridement to "bleeding tissue" may imply "excisional" but may not be precise enough, and should be clarified.

It may be documented by **any provider** (including healthcare professionals like nurses, physical therapists, physician assistants, podiatrists) who is licensed and credentialed to perform this procedure.

Sometimes during an incision and drainage (I&D) of an abscess, the provider may also perform significant debridement of necrotic tissue, so stay alert to this possible query opportunity.

Remember also that any debridement procedure is classified based on its greatest depth, so a procedure that extends below the subcutaneous tissue is not coded 86.22, but rather as a debridement of the fascia (83.44), muscle (83.45), bone (77.60-77.69), abdominal wall (54.3), joint, or other location.

Important: Recovery Auditors often attempt to recover payments when "excisional debridement" does not also document specifically the "cutting away of tissue," "cutting outside or beyond the wound margin," or the tissue layers/depth of debridement.

> Effective March 21, 2008, *Coding Clinic* stated specifically if "excisional debridement" is documented by the provider, assign code 86.22.

Coding Clinic also advises hospitals to "work with their providers to ensure that the documentation used to support excisional debridement clearly describes the procedure performed."

Continued —

Non-Excisional Debridement (86.28)

Cleaning, brushing, scrubbing, washing, irrigating of wound; chemical or enzymatic treatment; or minor trimming/scraping to remove fragments of dead tissue. The use of VersaJet™ without additional surgical "cutting away" of tissue is classified by ICD-9-CM as non-excisional debridement even though it usually requires general anesthesia and is performed in the operating room.

In every case of wound or decubitus care, search carefully for documentation of debridement in the progress notes and/or nursing notes, if there is no operative report. An order for a surgical tray may be the only clue that a procedure was performed.

References:

Coding Clinic *Second Quarter 2004, p. 5; First Quarter 2008, p. 3; Second Quarter 2000, p. 9; Fourth Quarter 2004, p. 138.*

ICD-10: *Excisional debridement is under the root operation of Excision, body part; non-excisional is Extraction, body part.*

For example:

- *Excision, skin of buttocks (0HB8XZZ)*
- *Extraction, skin of buttocks (0HD8XZZ)*

CHF; Must be "acute" to be principal
info for query:
BNP
TX
ECHO
chest X-Ray

Definition

A condition in which the heart fails to pump blood through the circulatory system as it should (inadequate cardiac output). This results in decreased blood flow to the kidneys, causing the kidneys to retain water and sodium, which then accumulates in the lungs, abdominal organs, and the lower extremities (edema). Common symptoms include shortness of breath (dyspnea) at rest or with exertion, and easy fatigability.

The function of the myocardium may be impaired by damage due to chronic ischemia, myocardial infarction, or progressive strain on the ventricles by damaged heart valves or prolonged, uncontrolled hypertension. Rarer causes of heart failure include myocarditis and hereditary cardiomyopathy.

Systolic / Diastolic Heart Failure

The patho-physiologic classification of heart failure as systolic, diastolic, or both ("combined") is used for determining the correct codes to be assigned and the severity of illness classification.

Systolic heart failure is characterized by:

- **Low ejection fraction < 40% is diagnostic**
- Dilated, weak heart/thin ventricular wall
- Decreased outflow of blood from the heart (impaired ventricular pumping function)
- Most common cause: coronary artery disease (ischemic cardiomyopathy)
- More common than diastolic failure
- Must be treated with an ACE inhibitor (ACEI) or angiotensin receptor blocker (ARB), unless contraindicated, because these drugs prolong and improve the quality of life, reduce complications, and lower hospitalization rates for patients with any component of systolic heart failure

Diastolic heart failure is characterized by:

- Normal (55%–70%) or elevated ejection fraction (EF)
- Echocardiogram demonstrates "diastolic dysfunction"
- Thickened myocardium/hypertrophic ventricle with strong contraction
- Low-capacity ventricular chamber
- Ventricle does not "relax" properly during diastole resulting in impaired filling with blood
- Common cause is uncontrolled hypertension (hypertensive cardiomyopathy) or ESRD

The distinction between systolic and diastolic dysfunction has clinical management implications as well. Diastolic failure often gets diagnostic and therapeutic short-shrift sometimes leading to ineffective treatment. Beta-blockers are typically first-line drugs for diastolic failure. Lasix is indicated for excess fluid accumulation, often absent with diastolic failure. Digoxin may be beneficial for patients with systolic failure but does little or nothing for diastolic dysfunction; it may of course be utilized for rate control of atrial fibrillation.

The clinical classification of the degree of heart failure is defined by the New York Heart Association (NYHA) Functional Classification:

Class	Functional Capacity
I	No limitations of physical activity
II	Comfortable at rest; ordinary activity causes symptoms
III	Comfortable at rest; less than ordinary activity causes symptoms
IV	Symptoms caused by any activity or at rest

* Add for NYHA query

ICD-9 and ICD-10 make no provisions for coding of the NYHA classification, which is based on acuity and the systolic/diastolic distinctions.

Diagnosis With Echocardiogram

An echocardiogram provides the ejection fraction and evaluates heart valves, blood flow, systolic/diastolic function, chamber size, ventricular wall motion, and thickness. If the ejection fraction is < 40% the diagnosis of systolic failure is confirmed. Any echocardiogram that does not assess the parameters for diastolic dysfunction and report accordingly should be considered incomplete.

Medications for Heart Failure

Diuretics are used to eliminate excesssive fluid accumulation, more commonly seen in systolic heart failure.

Examples include:

- Lasix (furosemide) is the usual choice
- Aldactone (spironolactone) may be used in severe/advanced heart failure because it reduces mortality
- Bumex (bumetanide)
- Zaroxolyn (metolazone)
- Hydrochlorothiazide (HCTZ)
- Maxzide/Dyazide (triamterene + HCTZ)

ACEI or ARB. Either an ACEI or ARB (rarely both in combination) is used for treatment of both systolic & diastolic heart failure:

- ACEI (Angiotensin-converting enzyme inhibitors) include Vasotec (enalapril), lisinopril, captopril, and others.

- ARB (Angiotensin II receptor blockers): Cozaar (losartan), Avapro, Diovan, Micardis, and others.

Beta-blockers are essential for systolic heart failure unless contraindicated. The primary focus of therapy for diastolic failure is the use of beta-blockers (combined with ACEI or ARB) to control hypertension. Beta-blockers slow the heart rate, lower blood pressure, reduce cardiac oxygen consumption, and lessen the cardiac workload.

Three beta-blockers have been shown to improve survival in heart failure:

- Coreg (carvedilol) – used almost exclusively for heart failure
- Toprol XL/Lopressor (metoprolol)
- Zebeta (bisoprolol)

Beta-blockers (generally metoprolol or atenolol) have many other uses, such as for hypertension and ischemic cardiac disease. Keep in mind that a patient with these conditions may also be receiving beta-blocker simultaneously for co-existing heart failure as well.

Digoxin improves the pumping ability of the heart in systolic heart failure, but does not benefit diastolic heart failure. The best-known brand name is Lanoxin.

Nitrates are beneficial for severe systolic heart failure but generally not recommended, or must be used with extreme caution, for diastolic failure since they may reduce diastolic filling resulting in lower cardiac output. Nitrates are venous and coronary artery vasodilators that reduce cardiac work, increase coronary blood flow, and improve cardiac performance. Examples include:

- Nitroglycerin (IV, transdermal, oral)
- Imdur (isosorbide mononitrite)
- Isordil (isosorbide dinitrate)

Hydralazine (an arterial vasodilator also used for the treatment of hypertension) is frequently combined with nitrates for severe systolic heart failure.

Calcium channel blockers (another class of anti-hypertensives) are not recommended for the routine treatment of heart failure.

Coding & Documentation Issues

The specification of systolic or diastolic failure or dysfunction is essential for proper coding of heart failure. When not the principal diagnosis, heart failure or "CHF" must be specified as systolic or diastolic to qualify as a CC (if not acute) or MCC when acute. The term systolic or diastolic "dysfunction" with any reference in the record to heart failure is specific enough for code assignment.

Stable, c[illegible] well-controlled, asymptomatic heart failure is conside[illegible] significant severity qualifying for CC status, [illegible] specified as systolic or diastolic.

When heart failure or "CHF" is the principal diagnosis, this specificity has no impact on the DRG; it is only relevant when a secondary diagnosis (CC or MCC).

Acute heart failure is obviously a much more serious and severe condition classified as an MCC. The terms exacerbation and decompensation are equivalent to "acute". Clinical indicators include:

- Exacerbation of symptoms including dyspnea/shortness of breath, tachypnea, respiratory distress, worsening edema, unstable angina
- IV medications (usually Lasix)
- Supplemental oxygen

- Pulmonary edema/congestion or increasing pleural effusion on chest x-ray
- BNP > 500 or Pro-BNP > 3000 (if no renal impairment)

The term "hypertensive cardiomyopathy with preserved ventricular function" may be used to describe diastolic heart failure, but this needs to be clarified for precise code assignment.

When pleural effusion is associated with heart failure, it is not separately coded unless requiring specific evaluation (such as decubitus chest x-rays or CT scan), treatment (like therapeutic thoracentesis) or attributed to another condition by the provider.

Fluid Overload Due to Dialysis Non-Compliance

When patients are admitted in CHF due fluid overload and non-compliance with dialysis treatment, CHF should be assigned as the principal diagnosis.

However, fluid overload should be assigned as principal diagnosis when a patient is admitted with fluid overload due to dialysis non-compliance and:

- The patient has no history or evidence of CHF, or
- The patient has a history of CHF, and the provider specifically indicates the fluid overload was non-cardiogenic in nature or the CHF was not decompensated.

Per *Coding Clinic* 2007, Q3, p. 11.

ICD-10: *No changes (I50.1–I50.9).*

B-20 : ICD 10

Definition of AIDS

AIDS is caused by Human Immunodeficiency Virus (HIV) infection with destruction of CD4+ T-lymphocytes that help mediate the body's immune response to infection.

The CDC definition of AIDS, also described as HIV Stage 3, is an HIV-positive patient with any one of the following:

1) Current or prior diagnosis of an AIDS-defining condition*, or
2) Current or prior CD4+ T-lymphocyte count < 200, or
3) Current or prior CD4+ T-lymphocyte count < 14% of total lymphocytes

*An AIDS-defining condition takes precedence over CD4+ counts.

The most frequent **AIDS-defining conditions** (some may be presumptively diagnosed) include the following:

- Bacterial infections, multiple or recurrent
- Candidiasis of esophagus, bronchi, trachea, or lungs
- Coccidioidomycosis
- Cryptococcosis, extrapulmonary
- Cryptosporidiosis, chronic intestinal (>1 month's duration)
- Cytomegalovirus disease (other than liver, spleen, or nodes) including retinitis
- Encephalopathy, HIV related
- Herpes simplex: chronic ulcers, bronchitis, pneumonitis, esophagitis
- Histoplasmosis, disseminated or extrapulmonary
- Kaposi sarcoma
- Lymphoma: Burkitt, immunoblastic, or brain (primary)
- TB and other mycobacterial infections

- Pneumocystis pneumonia
- Pneumonia, recurrent
- Progressive multifocal leukoencephalopathy (PML)
- Salmonella septicemia, recurrent
- Toxoplasmosis of brain
- Wasting syndrome attributed to HIV

ICD-9 and ICD-10 identify these AIDS-defining conditions as "symptomatic", so AIDS and symptomatic HIV mean the same thing for coding purposes.

The CDC recommends treatment with antiretroviral drugs of all HIV-positive patients, with or without AIDS, but recognizes that initiation of treatment may sometimes be postponed based on psycho-social factors and/or the physician's assessment of clinical circumstances. Therefore, treatment does not necessarily mean that the patient has progressed from HIV-positive to AIDS.

Antiretroviral drugs with abbreviations include:

3TC = lamivudine	FTC = emtricitabine
ABC = abacavir	IDV = indinavir
APV = amprenavir	LPV/r = lopinavir/ritonavir
ATV = atazanavir	MVC = maraviroc
d4T = stavudine	NFV = nelfinavir
ddC = zalcitabine	NVP = nevirapine
ddI = didanosine	RAL = raltegravir
DLV = delavirdine	RTV = ritonavir
DRV = darunavir	SQV = saquinavir
EFV = efavirenz	TDF = tenofovir
ENF = enfuvirtide	TPV = tipranavir
ETR = etravirine	ZDV = zidovudine
FPV = fosamprenavir	

Documentation and Coding

For coding purposes, AIDS (code 042) includes the terms:

- AIDS
- HIV disease
- ARC (AIDS-related complex), or
- HIV plus specific documentation of a current or prior AIDS-defining condition.

Documentation of "HIV" only, "HIV-positive", or "HIV illness" is not coded as AIDS.

Clear, correct and precise diagnosis and documentation of AIDS vs. HIV-positive only is necessary for coding, DRG assignment and severity of illness classification. It also has profound implications for the HIV-positive patient who may or may not have progressed to AIDS.

Code Assignment

- Code 042 – AIDS: If AIDS has ever been previously diagnosed and code 042 assigned, it must always be coded 042 on every single subsequent encounter and never again code V08.

- Code V08 – HIV-positive: Used when the patient has never been diagnosed with AIDS or an AIDS-defining condition. Also called "asymptomatic HIV" in ICD-9.

Important! Codes are only assigned for confirmed HIV – do not assign if documented as suspected, probable, possible.

Every encounter (inpatient or outpatient) where HIV or HIV-positive is documented must be clarified to determine whether the patient has been diagnosed with AIDS. If any prior records or other information indicates a diagnosis of AIDS or previous assignment of code 042, it must be brought to the attention of the patient's physicians for confirmation and correct coding.

DRG Assignment

AIDS (code 042) drives the DRG regardless of whether it is the principal or a secondary diagnosis when a patient is admitted with specific "AIDS-related" or "Major AIDS-related conditions". Note that these conditions are very similar to but not exactly the same as the CDC's diagnostic "AIDS-defining conditions" listed above.

Use of an encoder-grouper greatly simplifies coding and DRG assignment because these major and other related conditions are incorporated into the grouper logic.

In this situation, the admission will be assigned to one of the HIV DRGs:

- DRG 974–976: HIV with Major Related Condition
- DRG 977: HIV with or without Other Related Condition
- DRG 969–970: HIV with Extensive OR Procedure and Major or Other Related Condition

Major AIDS-Related Conditions are numerous but some important ones include:

Encephalopathy
Histoplasmosis
Candidiasis
Cryptococcus
Cytomegalovirus (CMV)
Organic mental disorders
Certain lymphomas
Pneumonia
Endocarditis
Encephalitis
Myelitis
Presenile dementia
Sarcomas (Kaposi's)
Sepsis

- Herpes zoster
- Herpes simplex (some)
- TB
- Toxoplasmosis

Some of the **Other AIDS-Related Conditions**:

- Lymphadenopathy
- Splenomegaly
- Hepatomegaly
- Nephrotic syndrome
- Glomerulonephritis
- Gastroenteritis/colitis
- Malnutrition
- Weight loss
- Malabsorption
- Vitamin deficiencies
- Volume depletion
- Fatigue/malaise
- Certain arthritis/arthropathy
- Several types of anemia
- Thrombocytopenia
- Neutropenia
- Certain febrile conditions
- Neuropathy/neuritis
- Retinopathy/blindness
- Fungal skin infections

Examples:

- AIDS patient admitted for pneumonia. The DRG assigned is: 976=AIDS with Major Related Condition without CC/MCC.

  AIDS drives the DRG whether listed as principal or secondary diagnosis, and pneumonia is not an MCC in this situation.

- AIDS patient admitted for dehydration. The DRG assigned is: 977=AIDS with or without Other Related Condition.

When the patient with AIDS is admitted for a condition that is not listed as one of the major or other AIDS-related conditions, the principal diagnosis is the **unrelated condition** and is assigned to the DRG for that condition. AIDS (042) is an MCC.

Example: A patient with AIDS is admitted for hip fracture requiring total hip replacement. The principal diagnosis is hip fracture with AIDS as MCC: DRG 469 (Major joint replacement of lower extremity with MCC).

HYPERTENSION, ACCELERATED

The terms "malignant" and "accelerated" hypertension are outdated and have been replaced for many years by other clinical terminology. However, because coding terminology has not caught up with current usage, these old terms are required for the correct documentation and coding of severe hypertension when it occurs as a secondary diagnosis.

Terms such as "hypertensive emergency," "hypertensive crisis," "hypertensive urgency," "severe hypertension," "malignant hypertension," and "accelerated hypertension" are all used in the literature and often overlap. Yet "accelerated," "malignant," or "necrotizing" hypertension are the only terms that will result in coding as a comorbidity/complication: 401.0 or categories 402–405 with 4th digit = "0".

Using only the terms "hypertensive urgency," "hypertensive emergency," or "hypertensive crisis" will result in assignment of nonspecific hypertension codes that do not accurately reflect the seriousness of the patient's condition.

Clinical Definition: A patient with hypertension that is consistent with "accelerated" or "malignant" should require urgent treatment (either IV or STAT oral dosing), have the same risks and clinical implications as urgent or emergent hypertension, and meet one of the following criteria:

- Systolic blood pressure (BP) > 180 mm Hg, or
- Diastolic BP > 110 mm Hg, or
- Symptoms attributable to the hypertension (e.g., headache, dyspnea, or chest pain), or
- End-organ involvement/damage (e.g., neurologic, renal, or cardiac damage)

Continued —

The following compares the criteria for accelerated or malignant hypertension with the more current terminology[1]:

- "Hypertensive urgency" is defined as severe elevation in BP > 180/110 mm Hg without progressive target organ dysfunction. Symptoms may be present, including severe headache, shortness of breath, nose bleed, or anxiety.
- "Hypertensive emergency" is usually symptomatic and characterized by severe elevations in BP (> 180/120 mm Hg) complicated by evidence of impending or progressive target organ dysfunction.
- "Hypertensive crisis" is used to describe the spectrum of severe, uncontrolled hypertension that includes both urgent and emergent hypertension, as described above.

Examples of how physician documentation may incorporate current clinical terminology with that needed to support correct coding include:

- "Accelerated hypertension with hypertensive emergency"
- "Hypertensive urgency due to accelerated hypertension"
- "Malignant hypertension causing severe hypertensive emergency"

ICD-10: *Hypertension specificity eliminated (only one code in ICD-10) except that with heart and/or kidney disease and secondary causes. Benign, accelerated, or malignant hypertension and hypertensive crisis, urgency, or emergency are currently assigned to code I10.*

[1] JNC-7 (The Seventh Report of the Joint National Committee on Prevention, Detection, Evaluation, and Treatment of High Blood Pressure). *JAMA* 2003; 289 (19): 2560–2572. Complete report available at *www.nhlbi.nih.gov.*

MALNUTRITION

Efforts to define malnutrition have resulted in various diagnostic criteria over the years, culminating most recently in an entirely new consensus definition (the **ASPEN** guidelines) published in the May 2012 *Journal of the Academy of Nutrition and Dietetics.* We will place these guidelines in the context of the traditional concept of malnutrition, and then discuss issues relevant to compliant coding.

Traditional Definition of Malnutrition

The traditional concept of clinical malnutrition is a **chronic** condition, the diagnosis and severity of which depends on the physician's clinical judgment, taking into consideration a constellation of findings, none of which in isolation is considered required or definitive:

- **Physical findings** such as emaciation, cachexia, or muscle/adipose wasting (e.g., temporal wasting, thenar atrophy).
- **Risk factors** such as cancer, chemotherapy, AIDS, alcoholism, end-stage disease processes, debilitation, residence in a skilled nursing facility, malabsorption syndromes, or other gastrointestinal and pancreatic disorders.
- **Biochemical markers** (not due to other causes) such as low albumin, prealbumin, cholesterol, transferrin, blood urea nitrogen/creatinine ratio, and/or anemia.
- **Body mass composition** such as low body mass index, low body weight relative to ideal or usual weight, and recent or progressive unintended weight loss.

BMI >40 is "morbid obesity" need this
<19 "malnutrion"

can't code under BMI - Dr. must add dx/name

Severity of Malnutrition

Once the diagnosis of malnutrition has been established using these indicators, severity may be classified as follows:

#	Criteria	Severe	Moderate	Mild
1	Albumin (g/dL) and/or Prealbumin (mg/dL)	< 2.0 < 5.0	≤ 2.5 < 10.0	≤ 3.0 < 15.0
2	Ideal body weight	< 70%	< 80%	< 90%
3	Usual body weight	< 75% or wt loss parameters*	< 85%	< 95%
4	BMI (kg/m²)	< 16	< 17	< 18.5
	ICD-9-Codes	**261, 262**	**263.0**	**263.1**

*Unintended weight loss of > 5% in one month, > 7.5% in 3 months, > 10% in 6 months, or > 20% in one year.

Notes:

- "Chronic" is defined as having a duration of three months or more.
- Degree of severity is determined by the highest severity category in which two or more criteria are met.
- The biomarkers albumin and prealbumin are considered together as one criterion, not two. Biomarkers have validity for severity designation but must be considered with caution because there are many other conditions that can cause acutely low biomarkers which should first be excluded, especially inflammatory states, acute illness and trauma.

- Codes for severe malnutrition are MCCs, whereas mild and moderate malnutrition are CCs.
- Unspecified malnutrition (code 263.9) has no criteria and is also a CC. The severity criteria above should be used to confirm the diagnosis or support a query for severity.

New ASPEN Guidelines for Malnutrition

The 2012 Academy/ASPEN consensus guidelines (ASPEN) derived from an effort to identify evidence-based, objective criteria encompassing a broad range of acute and chronic circumstances. It is intended to focus attention, which has been lacking, on the serious consequences of nutritional imbalance associated with acute illness and injury.

The ASPEN Malnutrition Consensus definition redefines adult malnutrition as "undernutrition", classifying it as severe or non-severe based on the presence of two or more of six characteristics in one of three contexts. ASPEN cannot distinguish between mild and moderate which are lumped together as non-severe.

The **six characteristics (criteria)** are:

1. Insufficient energy intake
2. Weight loss (or #5 below)
3. Loss of muscle mass
4. Loss of subcutaneous fat
5. Localized or generalized fluid accumulation that can mask weight loss (an alternative to #2)
6. Diminished functional status as measured by hand grip strength device

When two or more criteria are present in any of the 3 contexts, the patient is considered to have malnutrition, defined by ASPEN as "undernutrition".

The **three contexts** are:

1. **Chronic illness** (duration of 3 months or more) such as widespread metastatic cancer, severe malabsorption syndromes, HIV, or chemotherapy.
2. **Social/environmental circumstances** such as severe debilitation, the elderly living alone without social support, or lack of care.
3. **Acute illness or injury** (duration of < 3 months) such as GI surgery, multisystem trauma, intubation, prolonged vomiting, or limited oral food intake.

ASPEN Classification of Malnutrition (Undernutrition)

Two or more criteria in any of the 3 contexts:

	Acute		Chronic		Social/ Environmental	
Energy Intake	<75% for >7 days	≤ 50% for ≥ 5 days	<75% for ≥ 1 month	≤ 75% for ≥ 1 month	<75% for ≥ 3 months	≤ 50% for ≥ 1 month
Weight Loss*	1-2% in 1 week	>2% in 1 week	5% in 1 month	> 5% in 1 month	5% in 1 month	> 5% in 1 month
	5% in 1 month	>5% in 1 month	7.5% in 3 months	> 7.5% in 3 months	7.5% in 3 months	> 7.5% in 3 months
	7.5% in 3 months	>7.5% in 3 months	10% in 6 months	> 10% in 6 months	10% in 6 months	> 10% in 6 months
			20% in 1 year	> 20% in 1 year	20% in 1 year	> 20% in 1 year
Muscle Mass	Mild	Moderate	Mild	Severe	Mild	Severe
Subcut Fat	Mild	Moderate	Mild	Severe	Mild	Severe
Hand Grip	Not reduced	Measurably reduced	Not reduced	Measurably reduced	Not reduced	Measurably reduced

***Fluid accumulation / edema** masking weight loss (alternative to weight loss criterion)

- Acute context: Non-severe = mild / Severe = moderate to severe
- Chronic and social/environmental context: Non-severe = mild / Severe = severe

Documentation and Coding Issues raised by ASPEN

Although the ASPEN criteria for malnutrition in the contexts of "chronic illness" and "social/environmental circumstances" are completely consistent with the traditional definition of malnutrition and the current ICD-9-CM malnutrition codes (260, 261, 262, 263.0 to 263.9), the ASPEN criteria for malnutrition, or "undernutrition", in the context of "acute illness or injury" are entirely new.

- The diagnosis of malnutrition in an acute context is not **consistent** with ICD-9-CM or ICD-10-CM codes for malnutrition, which are based on the traditional concept of chronic malnutrition.
- Acute malnutrition has not been validated with respect to CC or MCC status.
- The ICD-9-CM code for "undernutrition" is 269.9, which is not assigned CC or MCC status.

Until "acute" undernutrition can be validated with respect to CC or MCC status, it may be prudent to use code 269.9 to properly describe this condition, rather than the malnutrition codes, to avoid regulatory scrutiny or challenges.

For example, a 200-pound patient requiring GI surgery who is unable to eat for 6 days and loses 5 pounds during that time would be classified by ASPEN as having "severe malnutrition" (code 261, an MCC). Or, take the case of an elderly woman with usual and current weight of 120 pounds who is admitted with severe pneumonia and poor appetite. She consumes less than 75% of her expected energy intake over 7 days in the hospital and loses 1.5 pounds. ASPEN would classify this as "non-severe" malnutrition – code 263.0 or 263.9, both CCs. Medicare and other payers are not likely to endorse assigning malnutrition codes in such circumstances.

Hospitals should establish coding and query policies dealing with these matters. At this time, appropriate queries could be based on the traditional malnutrition criteria or on the new ASPEN definitions. Consider carefully any documentation or query for malnutrition ("undernutrition") in the context of acute illness or injury, which might more appropriately be assigned to ICD-9-CM code 269.9.

There are also many ambiguities and inconsistencies in the ASPEN guidelines that need clarification.

References:

1. Academy/ASPEN Adult Malnutrition Consensus 2012: *J Acad Nutr Diet* 2012; 112: 730-738. http://malnutrition.andjrnl.org/Content/articles/1-Consensus_Statement.pdf
2. Jensen et al. Malnutrition Syndromes: A Conundrum vs Continuum. *J Parenter Enteral Nutr* 2009; 33(6):710-716. Available for purchase at: http://pen.sagepub.com/content/33/6/710.long
3. Cleveland Clinic Perioperative Nutritional Support – Who and How: *Cleve Clin J Med* 2004; 71: 345-351. www.ccjm.org/content/71/4/345.full.pdf+html
4. Cleveland Clinic Nutritional Issues in the Surgical Patient: *Cleve Clin J Med* 2006; 73: S77-S81. www.ccjm.org/content/73/Suppl_1/S77.full.pdf+html

MECHANICAL VENTILATION

Mechanical Ventilation (96.71, 96.72)

Mechanical ventilation is an invasive respiratory procedure that partially or fully supports a patient's respiratory function, moving air (usually supplemented with oxygen and/or aerosolized medications) into and out of the lungs. The ventilator is connected to the patient's airways by an endotracheal or tracheostomy tube.

Do not assign a code from category 96.7 unless the ventilator support is "invasive," i.e., delivered through an endotracheal tube (96.04) or a tracheostomy.

- 96.71: Continuous invasive mechanical ventilation < 96 hours
- 96.72: Continuous invasive mechanical ventilation 96+ hours

Other continuous invasive mechanical ventilation support via endotracheal tube or tracheostomy included in category 96.7 are:
- BiPAP delivered through an endotracheal tube or tracheostomy
- CPAP delivered through an endotracheal tube or tracheostomy

Although BiPAP and CPAP are often used to treat acute respiratory failure, these modalities are not usually included in category 96.7 since they are not typically delivered via an endotracheal tube or tracheostomy.

To calculate duration of mechanical ventilation:

Start time begins with the time of:

1. Endotracheal intubation (and subsequent initiation of mechanical ventilation)
2. Initiation of mechanical ventilation through a tracheostomy
3. Arrival time of a previously intubated patient or a patient with a tracheostomy who is already on mechanical ventilation

Considered part of the initial (continuous) duration:

1. Removal and immediate replacement of endotracheal tubes including immediate re-intubation following self-extubation.
2. Change from endotracheal intubation to a tracheostomy (mechanical ventilation is continued).
3. Weaning of a patient is included in counting the initial (continuous) duration. There may be several attempts to wean the patient prior to extubation, and there may be times when the ventilator is not in use even though the patient is still intubated.

Duration ends with:

1. Endotracheal extubation (the patient may be disconnected from the ventilator, but duration continues until the patient is extubated)
2. Cessation of the ventilator support for patients with a tracheostomy (termination of ventilator dependency)
3. Discharge/transfer time while still on the ventilator

Note: The tracheostomy tube may not be withdrawn for several days, or may be left in place indefinitely, after mechanical ventilation is discontinued. Therefore, the duration of mechanical ventilation would end with cessation of ventilator support prior to removal.

The patient may require a subsequent period(s) of mechanical ventilation during the same hospitalization, interrupted by a ventilator-free period(s). In this case, two (or more) separate codes from category 96.7 would be reported, each according to the duration of that particular period of continuous mechanical ventilation.

MECHANICAL VENTILATION

Postoperative mechanical ventilation: *Coding Clinic* states that a code for mechanical ventilation (and intubation) should not be assigned postoperatively for mechanical ventilation when it is considered a "normal part of surgery". The assumption is made that "**more than 2 days**" would always be considered longer than normally expected. Two days is taken to mean 48 hours. Begin counting from the time of intubation in the OR.

In addition, if the physician documents the patient is maintained on the ventilator longer than expected (when less than 2 days) due to a specific problem, a code for mechanical ventilation may be assigned.

This will rarely impact the DRG assignment since the DRG will be driven by the surgical procedure. This *Coding Clinic* advice relates only to the assignment of mechanical ventilation codes postoperatively, and not the diagnosis of respiratory failure.

> **ICD-10:** *PCS codes 5A19- expand duration to less than 24 hours, 24–96 hours, and greater than 96 hours.*

References:

Coding Clinic, Fourth Quarter 1991, p. 16–22
Second Quarter 1992, p. 13; Third Quarter 1998, p. 14;
First Quarter 2002, p. 12; Third Quarter 2004, p. 11;
Second Quarter 2006, p. 8; Fourth Quarter 2008, p. 187;
Third Quarter 2010, p. 3; First Quarter 2013, p. 12

Acute coronary syndrome (ACS) encompasses a continuum of myocardial ischemia and infarction. The American Heart Association (AHA)/American College of Cardiology (ACC) Guidelines for the Management of Patients with Unstable Angina/Non-ST-Elevation Myocardial Infarction (NSTEMI) define ACS as a provisional diagnostic term encompassing "clinical symptoms that are compatible with acute myocardial ischemia."

The Guidelines state that the provisional diagnosis of ACS should be further clarified following evaluation as:

1. STEMI (ST Elevation) or Q-wave myocardial infarction requiring consideration of immediate reperfusion therapy or percutaneous coronary intervention (PCI)
2. NSTEMI (Non-ST Elevation MI)
3. Unstable Angina (definite, probable, or possible)
4. Non-ACS cardiovascular condition (for example, pericarditis)
5. Non-cardiac condition with a specific cause (for example, GERD or costo-chondritis) or with unknown cause.

The more severe conditions of STEMI and Q-wave infarction which are usually self-evident and well documented are not discussed here.

NSTEMI and Unstable Angina (UA) are a part of the ACS continuum considered to have similar causes and clinical presentations, but different severity as defined by the release of cardiac biomarker(s) such as troponin I, troponin T or CK-MB.

The usual mechanism of ischemia is thrombosis due to coronary artery disease: a blood clot at the site of atherosclerotic plaque obstructing blood flow in the artery leaving the heart muscle without adequate blood flow. If the obstruction is severe enough to damage the muscle tissue (infarction), biomarkers are released; if no biomarkers are released the ischemia was less severe and damage did not occur.

According to the AHA/ACC Guidelines:

- "NSTEMI is established if a biomarker has been released," to a level above "the 99th percentile reference limit of the normal population."
- Unstable Angina is diagnosed when there is no biomarker release based on 2 samples collected at least 6 hours apart.

In other words, a CK-MB or troponin level above the 99th percentile of the lab test reference range is indicative of acute MI. It is therefore important to know what the 99th percentile reference range is for the hospital's lab (commonly 0.04 mcg/L, but ranging between 0.01–0.08 mcg/L depending on the assay method used).

False-Positive Troponin

Keep in mind the many causes of elevated troponin levels that do not necessarily indicate MI include: heart failure, renal failure, arrhythmias, myocarditis, pulmonary embolism, and uneventful coronary procedures. Clinical presentation and other diagnostic studies will help to rule out these alternative diagnoses.

Demand Ischemia

Where does demand ischemia fit into the picture? This term is often used indiscriminately to describe patients with evidence of myocardial ischemia associated with a mismatch between myocardial oxygen demand and supply, but without coronary artery disease (CAD) or at least not primarily due to CAD. The diagnosis of "demand ischemia" is sometimes used by physicians when patients experience release of cardiac biomarkers, like troponin.

However, *The Third Universal Definition of Myocardial Infarction* (*Circulation* 2012; 126: 2020-2035), developed jointly and published by the ACC, AHA, European Society of Cardiology and World Heart Foundation, defines "MI type 2" as: "myocardial injury with necrosis [recognized by cardiac biomarker release], where a condition other than CAD contributes to an imbalance between myocardial oxygen supply and/or demand."

Therefore, "demand ischemia" associated with release of cardiac biomarkers (troponin and/or CK-MB) to a level above the 99th percentile reference limit actually represents progression to myocardial infarction (such as NSTEMI) as defined by this authoritative professional consensus. This is also consistent with the AHA/ACS guidelines for UA/NSTEMI discussed above.

Examples of conditions involving myocardial oxygen supply/demand imbalance include:

- Tachy- and brady-arrhythmias
- Aortic dissection
- Severe aortic valve disease
- Hypertrophic cardiomyopathy
- Shock: cardiogenic, hypovolemic, septic
- Severe anemia
- Hypertensive crisis
- Coronary spasm
- Coronary embolism or vasculitis
- Coronary endothelial dysfunction without CAD

Prinzmetal's Variant Angina (PVA)

Prinzmetal's angina, often referred to as "variant" angina, represents transient myocardial ischemia (with ST-segment elevation) due to temporary coronary artery spasm (not thrombosis). It may occur with or without coronary artery disease (CAD), and is typically seen in young women without cardiac risk factors but may be linked to smoking.

PVA has been associated with other vasospastic disorders such as Raynaud's phenomenon and migraine headaches. Arrhythmias are common and may rarely be life threatening. In the absence of CAD, MI is unusual. When PVA is associated with CAD, the prognosis and risk of MI is determined by the severity of the underlying CAD. Biomarker release would not be expected unless myocardial damage (MI) has occurred.

Medical therapy typically employs vasodilator drugs, which include nitrates and calcium channel blockers. Beta-blockers, like atenolol and metoprolol, are not recommended because they may precipitate or worsen coronary vasospasm.

Coding Guidelines

Following the AHA/ACC guidelines, ICD-9 classifies Unstable Angina and ACS as the same condition: "Intermediate cardiac syndrome", code 411.1. NSTEMI, even if characterized as mild or "early", is classified as an acute MI.

As principal diagnosis, ACS and Unstable Angina are assigned to the low-weighted, low-severity DRG 311 Angina. NSTEMI is included in the high-weighted, high-severity DRGs 280-285 (Acute MI). As secondary diagnoses, ACS and Unstable Angina are CCs, and NSTEMI is an MCC.

Always query regarding the possibility of NSTEMI when the diagnosis of ACS, Unstable Angina, or demand ischemia is associated with an elevated troponin or CK-MB level since the AHA/ACC guidelines indicate that this is most likely an MI.

ICD-10: *I21.3 STEMI is the default code for acute myocardial infarction, unspecified.*

For encounters occurring for an acute MI that is ≤ 4 weeks old and the patient requires continued care for the MI, codes from Category I21 (acute MI) are assigned. Category I22 (subsequent MI) is used to code an acute MI occurring within 4 weeks of a previous MI.

Code I25.2 is used for any healing or old MI that does not require any continued care. If continued care is provided for an MI after 4 weeks, an aftercare code is assigned.

In ICD-9, an encounter occurring for an acute MI that was ≤ 8 weeks old was coded to "subsequent" episode of care. There are no ICD-9 codes to designate a "subsequent" MI.

References

1. The Third Universal Definition of Myocardial Infarction, *Circulation* 2012; 126: 2020-2035.
2. 2011 ACCF/AHA Focused Update of the Guidelines for the Management of Patients with Unstable Angina/Non–ST-Elevation Myocardial Infarction, *J Am Coll Cardiol* 2011;57: 1920-1959.
3. ACC/AHA 2007 Guidelines for the Management of Patients With Unstable Angina/Non ST-Elevation Myocardial Infarction, *Circulation*. 2007;116: e148-e304.

PALLIATIVE CARE—V66.7

Definition: Encounter for palliative care, includes end-of-life care, hospice care, comfort care, or terminal care.

Code V66.7 should be assigned as a secondary diagnosis when a patient is placed in hospice care, or when a patient is admitted for an acute condition but it is subsequently determined that the patient is no longer a candidate for aggressive therapy or surgery and receives supportive and comfort care only.

Per *Coding Clinic,* Third Quarter 2008, p. 13, code V66.7 "may be reported for any terminally ill patient who receives palliative care, regardless as to when the decision is made. There is no time limit or minimum for the use of this code assignment."

Palliative care is an alternative to aggressive treatment for patients who are in the terminal phase of their illness. Palliative care is focused towards management of pain and symptoms, and is often more appropriate than aggressive hospital treatment for patients dying of incurable diseases. The physician documentation in the medical record must substantiate that palliative care is being given. Terms such as comfort care, end-of-life care, and hospice care are all synonymous with palliative care. These, or similar terms, need to be written in the record to support the use of code V66.7. Designation of "DNR" status alone is not sufficient.

The physician should be queried if the treatment record seems to indicate that palliative care is being given but the documentation is unclear. The care provided must be aimed only at relieving pain and discomfort for the palliative care code to be applicable.

While this diagnosis code **does not affect DRG assignment,** it often affects mortality profiles and should be coded when appropriate.

See also *Coding Clinic,* Third Quarter 2010, p. 18, and First Quarter 1998, p. 11.

ICD-10: *Code Z51.5.*

Definition

Pancreatitis is inflammation of the pancreas not typically associated with infection. It can be acute or chronic; it may be mild or severe and potentially life-threatening. It may be caused by: alcoholism, elevated triglycerides (especially with diabetes), hypercalcemia, medications and gallstone obstruction of the pancreatic duct, i.e. gallstone pancreatitis.

Inflammation of the pancreas is unusually dangerous because the pancreas produces digestive enzymes. When released during pancreatitis, these enzymes cause extreme tissue destruction. Pancreatic duct obstruction is particularly serious resulting in potentially life-threatening cholangitis and sustained acute pancreatitis.

Acute Pancreatitis

Symptoms include acute abdominal/back pain; often fever, elevated white blood cell count, vomiting; sometimes with hypocalcemia, ileus, or acute kidney injury. Pancreatic enzymes amylase and lipase are usually both elevated.

The American College of Gastroenterology recommends that 2 of the following 3 findings would usually indicate acute pancreatitis:

- Abdominal pain consistent with pancreatitis
- Lipase and/or amylase > 3 times upper limit of normal
- Characteristic findings on imaging studies (ultrasound, CT, MRI)

Ultrasound is usually performed for possible pancreatic duct obstruction due to gallstones.

Treatment may include IV pain medication, IV fluid resuscitation, NPO/NG-suction; sometimes IV antibiotics (if infection is suspected). It may require magnetic resonance cholangio-pancreatography (MRCP) or diagnostic/therapeutic endoscopic retrograde cholangiopancreatography (ERCP).

Acute pancreatitis may lead to chronic pancreatitis, pancreatic insufficiency, pseudocyst or abscess. Mortality from acute pancreatitis ranges from 2-9% with higher risk if age > 55, BMI > 30, organ failure, or alcoholism.

When a patient has acute pancreatitis it is usually the principal diagnosis but is an MCC if a secondary diagnosis. It should be distinguished from chronic pancreatitis.

Chronic Pancreatitis

The usual manifestation of chronic pancreatitis is chronic abdominal pain requiring chronic opioid analgesics. Tobacco and alcohol cessation are recommended. Amylase may be normal but lipase is a more sensitive test and usually elevated. Recurrent acute exacerbations are characteristic which may require inpatient admission.

Chronic pancreatitis may result in pancreatic insufficiency requiring long-term oral enzyme replacement such as Creon, Pancrease, Viokase, Zenpep.

It can cause secondary diabetes due to destruction of insulin-producing pancreatic islet cells. In up to 10% of cases, patients may develop pancreatic pseudocyst or pancreatic cancer (the 20-year risk is 5%).

Chronic pancreatitis is not typically the principal reason for admission unless there is an acute exacerbation (577.0).

Pancreatic Pseudocyst or Cyst

Pancreatic pseudocyst or "cyst" develops in up to 10% of patients with chronic pancreatitis. Usually asymptomatic, it is typically diagnosed with CT scan. It may require drainage, often done percutaneously, if it is large (greater than 6-12cm), symptomatic or complicated by infection, abscess, fistula, ascites, or biliary obstruction. Pancreatic cancer also has to be considered as a possibility.

References

Management of Acute Pancreatitis. Am J Gastroenterol 2013; 108:1400–1415. Available at: http://gi.org/guideline/acute-pancreatitis

Cleveland Clinic: Acute Pancreatitis. Available at: http://www.clevelandclinicmeded.com/medicalpubs/diseasemanagement/gastroenterology/acute-pancreatitis

Clinical Manifestations and Diagnosis of Acute Pancreatitis (May 2013). Up-to-Date available at: www.uptodate.com

PATHOLOGIC FRACTURES

Definition*: A pathologic fracture is defined as a fracture due to abnormal underlying bone with minimal or no trauma.

The trauma literature defines significant trauma, among other things, as a fall from a height of six feet or more. Therefore, simply falling from a sitting or standing position ordinarily does not qualify as significant trauma.

The ICD-9-CM Index to Diseases indicates that any fracture is classified as a pathologic fracture (code 733.1x) if specified as "due to" osteoporosis (osteoporotic), neoplasm (malignant), or other bone diseases; or if documented as "insufficiency," "spontaneous," or "chronic" fracture.

Any "stress fracture" (733.93–733.98) as principal diagnosis will also be assigned to DRGs 542–544 (Pathologic Fracture).

Vertebral Compression Fractures: When a patient is admitted with an "acute compression fracture" of a vertebral body as principal diagnosis, it is classified as a "traumatic" fracture and assigned to DRG 551/552, Medical Back Problems, unless an operative procedure is performed.

On the other hand, most patients who are hospitalized for this problem are elderly or debilitated, frequently have severe osteoporosis, and did not experience significant trauma (even though they often have had a minor fall either recently or acutely).

* *J Neurosurg Spine* 7: 305–310, 2007.

Continued —

Under these circumstances the most accurate and specific diagnosis is usually not "traumatic" but rather pathologic (including non-traumatic, insufficiency, spontaneous, chronic) or osteoporotic vertebral fracture (DRGs 542–544). "Collapsed vertebra" is also coded as a pathologic fracture (733.13).

Diagnosis and Treatment: Look for treatment of osteoporosis with medications like Fosamax, Boniva, Actonel, Reclast, Evista, vitamin D, calcium supplements, and/or calcitonin (Fortical and Miacalcin).

DEXA scanning is the usual diagnostic tool for osteoporosis; it does not need to be repeated if a prior diagnosis of osteoporosis has been made, especially if the patient is being treated for osteoporosis.

Important: Osteoporosis has already become **severe** if it can be identified on plain x-ray studies; radiologists will often use the term "osteopenia." Even mild osteopenia on plain x-ray represents severe underlying osteoporosis.

As a **secondary diagnosis,** the distinction between compression (traumatic) and pathologic (non-traumatic) fracture does not affect DRG assignment; both are classified as CCs. In either case, it should be an acute or subacute condition requiring care/treatment/evaluation, not just an old or incidental finding on x-ray, to justify code assignment.

ICD-10: *Official Coding Guidelines: "A code from category M80 [Osteoporosis with current pathological fracture], not a traumatic fracture code, should be used for any patient with known osteoporosis who suffers a fracture, even if the patient had a minor fall or trauma, if that fall or trauma would not usually break a normal, healthy bone."*

PNEUMONIA

Definition

Pneumonia generally refers to lung infection with inflammatory exudation into the alveolar air spaces ("consolidation" or "infiltrate").

Pneumonia is most commonly caused by viruses or bacteria, but other causes include fungi, parasites, chemicals, toxins, or physical injury to the lungs.

The term "pneumonitis" generally refers to an inflammatory reaction without consolidation and without implying causation, which may be infectious, allergic, toxic, or irritant in nature, but is coded as "pneumonia", if not otherwise specified.

Symptoms

Cough, difficulty breathing, sputum production, variable degrees of shortness of breath, pleuritic chest pain and fever. Respiratory distress can progress to respiratory failure, which may be the principal reason for admission, depending upon the circumstances of the case.

Diagnosis

Pneumonia is a clinical diagnosis based on the findings and circumstances (not on cultures). Chest x-ray or CT scan is confirmatory and usually shows consolidation or infiltrate, which may be delayed in appearance by one or two days, especially if the patient is initially dehydrated.

A CT scan is more accurate than chest x-ray and may occasionally demonstrate infiltrate(s) when chest x-ray does not. However, it is rarely necessary to perform a CT scan for uncomplicated pneumonia.

When imaging studies are unremarkable, pneumonia may be diagnosed on clinical grounds alone (symptoms and/or findings of congestion, rales, "crackles," or rhonchi in the lungs). To ensure audit compliance, the provider ought to make a specific reference to the clinical basis of the diagnosis also noting the absence of radiographic findings.

WBC may be low, normal, or elevated; if less than 4,000 or more than 12,000 (or if the differential count includes > 10% band-forms), sepsis should be considered.

Blood and sputum cultures are often performed in an attempt to isolate the causative organism(s); but these are notoriously inaccurate, usually negative, occasionally falsely positive, and subject to clinical interpretation. Remember that diagnostic codes for inpatients are never assigned based solely on laboratory reports.

Types of Pneumonia

Evidence-based professional guidelines classify pneumonia into four types, which determine the likely organism(s) involved, appropriate antibiotic selection, and patient management:

- **Community-acquired pneumonia (CAP)**, which is acquired in the community without healthcare contact
- **Healthcare-associated pneumonia (HCAP)**, which is acquired outside the hospital but in connection with other healthcare contact
- **Hospital-acquired pneumonia (HAP)**, which is acquired during hospitalization (including patients readmitted within 48 hours with a "new" pneumonia)

- **Ventilator-associated pneumonia** (VAP), which typically develops 48 hours or more after mechanical ventilation is initiated and usually hospital acquired

However, the ICD-9-CM coding classification of pneumonia is based on causation (organisms or aspiration) and does not recognize the clinical classifications of CAP, HCAP, or HAP. In order to be assigned the appropriate codes, the provider must identify the probable, likely, possible, suspected, or definitive organism causing the pneumonia.

Community-Acquired Pneumonia (CAP)

CAP is usually caused by Pneumococcus, Hemophilus, Chlamydia, or Mycoplasma, or by viruses. Mortality rates should be low (about 2%).

It is typically treated with one or more of the following antibiotics depending on whether the patient is admitted to an ICU: Rocephin, Zithromax, doxycycline, or a fluoroquinolone (e.g., Levaquin or Avelox).

Healthcare-Associated Pneumonia (HCAP)

Patients with HCAP are most likely to have gram-negative and possibly staphylococcal infection, including MRSA and other drug-resistant organisms. Treatment with multiple, broad-spectrum antibiotics such as Zosyn, cefepime, imipenem, gentamicin, vancomycin, Zyvox, and others is required.

Circumstances associated with HCAP:

- Hospitalization for two days or more within the last 90 days
- Residence in skilled nursing, long-term acute care, inpatient rehab, etc.

- Attendance at a dialysis clinic, oncology clinic, wound care clinic, or outpatient infusion center
- Intravenous antibiotic therapy, chemotherapy, or wound care within the past 30 days
- Home healthcare with IV or wound care

Patients with HCAP require extensive utilization of resources at high cost and have high rates of morbidity and mortality (about 10%–20%). Therefore, HCAP would be most appropriately assigned to DRGs 177–179 (Respiratory Infections), but will not be unless the physician documents what organisms are probable or suspected as the cause, or that the pneumonia is due to aspiration.

Physicians often do not document the **suspected** cause/organism clearly and may simply diagnose "pneumonia," even though appropriate broad-spectrum antibiotics are given. The undesirable result is the classification of a severe, potentially life-threatening condition as a simple pneumonia. When this happens, a query for further specificity or clarification of the cause is essential.

The terms "coverage" or "coverage for" certain organisms are not adequate documentation for coding purposes; the suspected organism or organisms must be specifically mentioned as a possible cause.

References: *Am J Respir Crit Care Med* 2005; 171: 388–416; *Clinical Infectious Diseases* 2008; 46: S296–334.

Hospital-Acquired Pneumonia (HAP)

HAP is a specific type of HCAP associated with even greater risks and severity. It is nearly always caused by gram-negative organisms or staph (or perhaps unrecognized aspiration). The organisms involved in HAP are frequently resistant to multiple antibiotics. HAP is clinically defined as pneumonia that occurs 48 hours or more after admission and was not incubating at the time of admission.

For reporting purposes, CMS identifies any hospital-acquired infection including HAP as one that was not present or incubating at the time of admission, or if a patient is readmitted with a new infection within 48 hours of discharge. As with HCAP, ICD-9-CM does not recognize HAP, which will default to Simple Pneumonia, NOS (486) unless the cause is further specified.

Ventilator-Associated Pneumonia (VAP)

VAP is usually hospital-acquired but can occur in patients who are chronically ventilator dependent. VAP is defined clinically as pneumonia that develops 48 hours or more after mechanical ventilation is initiated by means of an endotracheal tube or tracheostomy. Causative organisms are usually Pseudomonas or staph (especially MRSA) and sometimes other gram-negatives.

Official Coding Guidelines state that code 997.31 (VAP) should be assigned only when the provider has specifically documented "ventilator associated pneumonia or VAP."

Pneumonia is classified into two primary MS-DRG groups:

1. Simple Pneumonia and Pleurisy (DRG 193–195)
2. Respiratory Infections (DRG 177–179)

Because the MS-DRG system classifies pneumonias on the basis of causation and does not recognize evidence-based clinical definitions, physician documentation often results in the clinically inappropriate assignment of a serious, life-threatening pneumonia (HCAP) to a Simple Pneumonia DRG.

Simple Pneumonia (DRG 193–195)

The following terminology will result in the classification of a simple pneumonia:

- Pneumonia, unspecified (code 486)
- Atypical* (code 486)
- Bronchopneumonia (code 485)
- Community-acquired (CAP), healthcare-associated (HCAP), hospital-acquired (HAP), or other similar "nosocomial" terms (code 486)
- Specified as viral, pneumococcal (streptococcal), Mycoplasma, Chlamydia, or Hemophilus influenzae

Codes 486 and 485 are NOS (not otherwise specified) codes, which cannot be assigned when a more specific diagnosis has been documented.

*When physicians use the term "atypical" pneumonia, it usually implies viral, Mycoplasma, or Chlamydia.

Respiratory Infections (DRG 177–179)

Based on clinical definitions, most healthcare-associated (HCAP) and hospital-acquired (HAP) pneumonias should fall into this DRG group. However, the correct codes that describe these conditions will not be assigned unless the physician is very specific regarding causation such as the likely, probable, or suspected organism(s) or aspiration pneumonia.

Aspiration pneumonia and the following organisms are assigned to the Respiratory Infection DRGs:

E. coli	Gram-negative	Proteus
Enterobacter	Klebsiella	Pseudomonas
Fungal	MRSA	Staphyloccocus

Tuberculosis (mycobacterium), Serratia, and anaerobes are also assigned to these DRGs.

Clinical Documentation Tips for Pneumonia

Aspiration Pneumonia

Aspiration pneumonia is more common than generally believed and often overlooked. Clinical indicators suggesting aspiration are:

- Debilitated, nursing home- or bed-confined
- Recent vomiting
- Presence of NG tube
- History of CVA
- Impaired gag reflex, dysphagia, or GERD
- Esophageal disorder (obstruction, stenosis, cancer)
- Positive swallowing study
- Alcoholic
- RLL infiltrate is "classic" location

Post-procedural aspiration pneumonia is coded to 997.32.

Antibiotic treatment ought to include Clindamycin, Zosyn, or Flagyl. Sometimes only antibiotics for simple pneumonia are ordered, so a query for aspiration pneumonia may be appropriate if not documented and there are indicators of aspiration.

Staphylococcal/MRSA Pneumonia

Clinical Indicators:

- Indwelling IV catheter/device, G tube
- ESRD, open wound/skin ulcers, postop, immune-suppressed, ventilator status
- Recent antibiotic therapy (especially broad-spectrum)
- Treatment with Vancomycin (sometimes Zyvox for MRSA)

Gram-Negative Pneumonia

Includes E. coli, Klebsiella, Proteus, Serratia, Pseudomonas, Enterobacter, and others.

Clinical Indicators:

- Elderly, debilitated, or nursing home resident
- Cancer, chemotherapy, other immuno-suppression
- COPD
- Ventilator status
- Chronic illness
- Recently hospitalized (especially ICU)
- Recent antibiotic therapy
- Pseudomonas: structural lung disease (like bronchiectasis)

Treatment includes Zosyn, Gentamicin, Tobramycin, Amikacin, Ceftazidime/Fortaz, Cefepime/Maxipime, Aztreonam/Azactam, Cipro.

Antibiotic Selection

Look for the antibiotics used to treat the pneumonia. Unfortunately, accurate culture results are difficult to obtain and are diagnostic in only about 20% of cases. Therefore, causation is usually a clinical determination. The best way to tell what organisms a physician is treating as the most likely, probable, or suspected cause of pneumonia are the antibiotics ordered.

Pneumonia as a Secondary Diagnosis: Most forms of pneumonia will qualify as an MCC. Notable exceptions are ventilator-associated pneumonia (VAP), post-procedural aspiration pneumonia, and that due to fumes/vapors, which are CCs.

> **ICD-10:** *Pneumonia specificity is based on organism or aspiration and essentially unchanged (J12.0–J18.9, J69.0–J69.8). Unspecified pneumonia is J18.9.*

PRESSURE (DECUBITUS) ULCERS

Definition and Cause: Ischemic necrosis of skin due to pressure from lying immobile for more than two hours. The contact pressure against a surface exceeds the capillary-filling pressure of the skin, preventing blood flow to the dermis.

Because of this causal relationship with pressure, decubitus ulcers most frequently occur in contact-point locations: back of the head, shoulder blades, elbows, low back, sacrum/coccyx, buttocks (gluteus), heels. If the patient is positioned to the left or right side for prolonged periods, decubiti may be found on the lateral shoulder; over the greater trochanter (lateral hip); medial or lateral ankles; and occasionally the lateral knee. Moisture, shear forces, and friction also contribute to decubitus formation.

Once the protective dermal layer is lost the necrosis may rapidly extend to subcutaneous tissue, muscle, and bone, sometimes resulting in osteomyelitis (bone infection). Ulcers beyond Stage I almost invariably become colonized with bacteria (usually staphylococcus, streptococcus, and gram negatives); can easily become infected, leading to cellulitis, gangrene, or abscess; and often progress to systemic infection with sepsis.

Every patient should be screened for decubitus ulcers at the time of admission; when found, they must be documented and treated. Decubitus ulcers should be distinguished from other forms of cutaneous ulceration such as diabetic, ischemic, stasis (venous), varicose, malignant, traumatic, atrophic, infectious (as cause), burns, unspecified.

Risk Factors: Inability to reposition self, debilitated, dehydration, malnutrition, bed or chair-confined, sensory deficits, fecal/urinary incontinence, inability to feed self.

Treatment: The treatment of advanced stages (Stage III & IV) is individualized according to extent, nature, severity, and complications, including excision and debridement of devitalized/necrotic tissue; wet-to-dry saline or hypochlorite solution packing/dressings; topical antibiotics; specialized gels; vacuum-assisted closure sponges; whirlpool treatment.

Classification: Pressure ulcers are classified as follows:

Stage I: Non-blanching erythema of the skin (redness that does not turn pale when pressed and released with a fingertip) with intact skin (no dermal ulceration)

Stage II: Partial thickness ulceration and loss of epidermis with abrasion, blister, or shallow ulcer

Stage III: Full-thickness ulceration into subcutaneous fat; may extend up to but not through deep fascia

Stage IV: Deep ulceration to muscle, tendons, joint, and/or bone (often with osteomyelitis); extensive tissue necrosis/destruction

Coding of Pressure Ulcers: Stage and Location

Pressure (decubitus) ulcers are coded by stage and location. The physician/provider must specifically document the presence, location, and POA status of decubitus ulcers. The stage can be documented by non-physicians: "For … pressure ulcer **stage** codes, code assignment may be based on medical record documentation from clinicians who are not the patient's provider … [since] nurses often document the pressure ulcer stages." See Official Guidelines Section I.B.16.

Two codes are assigned, one for the location (707.00–707.07, 707.09) and another for the stage (707.20–707.25). Stages III & IV (707.23, 707.24) are MCCs.

Unstageable: A scab or eschar forming on the surface may obscure the true extent of the ulcer, which is considered "unstageable." These must be debrided promptly for correct staging and treatment.

Deep tissue injury (DTI) involves necrosis of subcutaneous fat and/or deep fascia/muscle while the skin still remains intact (is not yet "ulcerated"). With DTI, necrosis of the skin is inevitable and this condition requires extensive deep excisional debridement of all necrotic tissue.

PRESSURE (DECUBITUS) ULCERS

Do not confuse "unstageable" (707.25) with "unspecified" (707.20), which is assigned when there is no documentation regarding stage. Pressure ulcer stage codes are used as secondary diagnoses and with decubitus ulcers only, never as principal diagnosis or with other types of ulcers (e.g., stasis or diabetic ulcers).

Stage III and IV decubitus ulcers that are designated as **not present on admission** (POA indicator = "N" or "U") will not qualify as an MCC under MS-DRGs. There is no required time frame as to when a provider must identify or document a condition to be present on admission.

Healed decubitus ulcers: No code is assigned if a decubitus ulcer is documented as "healed."

Healing decubitus ulcer: Decubitus ulcers described as "healing" should be assigned the appropriate stage code based on the documentation in the medical record.

Progression*: If a patient is admitted with a pressure ulcer at one stage and it progresses to a higher stage, assign the code for the highest stage reported for that site. In this case, assign POA indicator = "Y" for both the stage and location.

*Coding Clinic, *Fourth Quarter 2008, p. 194, and First Quarter 2009, p. 19.*

See Official Guidelines, Section I.C.12.a., Section I.B.16, and Appendix I: Present on Admission Reporting Guidelines.

ICD-10: *No significant changes except expanded combination codes for location, stage, and laterality (category L89).*

Definition: Severe respiratory/pulmonary dysfunction resulting in abnormalities of oxygenation or carbon dioxide gas (CO2) elimination.

Respiratory failure can result from abnormal gas exchange in the alveoli, a failure of ventilation (impairment of airflow in and out of the lungs), or both.

Respiratory failure is classified as hypoxemic (low arterial oxygen levels), hypercapneic (elevated levels of CO2), or a combination of the two. In most cases one or the other predominates.

Acute Respiratory Failure

It should be self-evident that a patient with acute respiratory failure ought to have some difficulty breathing such as: shortness of breath, dyspnea, tachypnea (respiratory rate > 20), respiratory distress, labored breathing, use of accessory muscles, cyanosis, etc.

The clinical criteria for diagnosing acute respiratory failure are based on blood gases:

- **Hypoxemic**
  - **pO2 < 60mmHg (SpO2 < 91%)** on room air, or
  - **pO2/FIO$_2$ (P/F) ratio < 300**, or
  - 10 mmHg decrease in baseline pO$_2$ (if known)

- **Hypercapnic**
  - **pCO2 > 50mmHg with pH < 7.35**, or
  - 10 mmHg increase in baseline pCO$_2$ (if known)

Other than the P/F ratio, these criteria have also been offered as assistance to coders and documentation specialists for recognizing possible acute respiratory failure (see *Coding Clinic* 1988 Q3, p. 7 and 1990 Q2, p. 20).

Management that requires endotracheal intubation and mechanical ventilation or initiation of BiPAP nearly always means the patient has acute respiratory failure, but these are not required for the diagnosis. Similarly, providing 40% or more supplemental oxygen implies that the physician is treating acute respiratory failure since only a patient with acute respiratory failure would need that much oxygen.

Arterial Blood Gas (ABG) is reported in a standard format: pH / pCO2 / pO2. The report should also show the amount of supplemental oxygen the patient was receiving when the ABG was drawn indicated as FIO2 (fraction of inspired oxygen).

- pH (normal = 7.35-7.45) – degree of acidity; lower pH is more acid (acidosis)
- pCO2 (normal = 35-45) – partial pressure (proportion or amount) of carbon dioxide gas
- pO2 (normal = 80-100) – partial pressure of oxygen

FIO2 (fraction or percent of inspired oxygen) is reported as a decimal that indicates the amount of oxygen the patient is breathing (e.g., FIO2 = 0.40 means 40% O2). If FIO2 is not on the report, the amount of supplemental oxygen can usually be identified elsewhere in the record.

Acute Hypoxemic Respiratory Failure

The gold standard for the diagnosis of hypoxemic respiratory failure is an **arterial pO_2** (partial pressure of oxygen) **on room air less than 60mmHg** measured by arterial blood gases (ABG). In the absence of an ABG, oxygen saturation (SpO2) measured by pulse oximetry on room air can serve as a substitute for the pO_2: SpO_2 of 91% equals pO_2 of 60mmHg.

These criteria may not apply to patients with chronic respiratory failure (e.g., severe COPD), because their room air pO_2 is often less than 60mmHg (SpO_2 < 91%). They are treated chronically with supplemental oxygen on a continuous outpatient basis to keep arterial oxygen above these levels. However, if the baseline pO_2 is known, a decrease by 10mmHg or more indicates acute hypoxemic respiratory failure in such a patient.

The Power of the P/F Ratio

The P/F ratio is a powerful objective tool to identify acute hypoxemic respiratory failure at any time while the patient is receiving supplemental oxygen, a frequent problem faced by documentation specialists where no room air ABG is available or pulse ox readings seem equivocal.

The P/F ratio equals the arterial pO2 ("P") from the ABG divided by the FIO2 ("F") – the fraction (percent) of inspired oxygen that the patient is receiving expressed as a decimal (40% oxygen = FIO2 of 0.40).

A P/F ratio less than 300 indicates acute respiratory failure.

Many physicians are unfamiliar with the P/F ratio, but it has been validated and used in the context of ARDS for many years, where acute respiratory failure is called "acute lung injury." A P/F ratio < 300 indicates mild ARDS, < 200 is consistent with moderate ARDS and < 100 is severe ARDS. The P/F ratio indicates what the pO2 would be on room air:

P/F ratio **< 300** is equivalent to a **pO_2 < 60 mm Hg** on room air
P/F ratio **< 250** is equivalent to a **pO_2 < 50 mm Hg** on room air
P/F ratio **< 200** is equivalent to a **pO_2 < 40 mm Hg** on room air

Example: Suppose the pO2 is 90mmHg on 40% oxygen (FIO2 = .40). The P/F ratio = 90 divided by .40 = 225. The pO2 on room air in this case would have been about 45 mmHg (well below the "cut-off" of 60mmHg for "respiratory failure").

The validity of the P/F ratio is not limited to ARDS. It simply expresses a consistent physiologic relationship between inspired oxygen and arterial pO_2 regardless of the cause. Authoritative applications of the P/F ratio in settings other ARDS include pneumonia and sepsis. The Infectious Disease Society of America and American Thoracic Society recognize a P/F ratio less than 250 as one of the 10 criteria for "severe" community-acquired pneumonia that may require admission to intensive care. The International Sepsis Definition criteria (2001) and the Surviving Sepsis - Severe Sepsis Guidelines (2008 and 2012) use a P/F ratio < 300 as an indicator of acute organ (respiratory) failure.

The P/F ratio should not be used to diagnose acute-on-chronic respiratory failure since many patients with chronic respiratory failure already have a P/F ratio <300 (pO2 <60 mmHg) in their baseline stable state. That's the reason they are treated with chronic supplemental home oxygen.

SpO2 translated to pO2

The arterial pO_2 measured by arterial blood gas (ABG) is the definitive method for calculating the P/F ratio. However, when the pO2 is unknown because an ABG is not available, the **SpO_2 measured by pulse oximetry** can be used to approximate the pO2, as shown in the table below. It is important to note that estimating the pO2 from the SpO2 becomes unreliable when the SpO2 is 98%–100%.

Conversion of SpO2 to pO2

SpO2 (percent)	pO2 (mm Hg)
86	51
87	52
88	54
89	56
90	58
91	60

SpO2 (percent)	pO2 (mm Hg)
92	64
93	68
94	73
95	80
96	90
97	110

Note: The SpO2/pO2 conversion becomes unreliable when SpO2 is > 97%.

Example: Suppose a patient on 40% oxygen has a pulse oximetry SpO_2 of 95%. Referring to the table above, SpO_2 of 95% is equal to a pO_2 of 80mmHg. The P/F ratio = 80 divided by 0.40 = 200. The patient may be stable receiving 40% oxygen, but still has severe acute respiratory failure. If oxygen were withdrawn leaving her on room air, the pO_2 would only be 40 mmHg (much less than the cut-off for acute respiratory failure of 60 mmHg on room air).

Translating Supplemental Oxygen: FIO2 (percent) and liters per minute

Supplemental oxygen may be administered either by mask or by nasal cannula ("NC"). A **Venturi mask** (Venti-mask) delivers a controlled flow of oxygen at a specific fixed concentration (FIO2): 24%, 28%, 31%, 35%, 40%, and 50%. The **non-rebreather ("NRB") mask** is designed to deliver approximately 100% oxygen. Providing 40% or more supplemental oxygen implies that the physician is treating acute respiratory failure since only a patient with acute respiratory failure would need that much oxygen.

A **nasal cannula** provides oxygen at adjustable flow rates in liters of oxygen per minute (L/min or "LPM"). The actual FIO2 (percent oxygen) delivered by nasal cannula is somewhat variable and less reliable than with a mask, but can be estimated as shown in the table below. The FIO2 derived from nasal cannula flow rates can then be used to calculate the P/F ratio.

Flow Rate	FIO2	Flow Rate	FIO2
1 L/min	24%	4 L/min	36%
2 L/min	28%	5 L/min	40%
3 L/min	32%	6 L/min	44%

Assumes room air is 20% and each L/min of oxygen = +4%.

Example: A patient has a pO2 of 85mmHg on ABG while receiving 5L/min of oxygen. Since 5L/min is equal to 40% oxygen (an FIO_2 of 0.40), the P/F ratio = 85 divided by 0.40 = 212.5.

Acute Hypercapneic Respiratory Failure

Definition: The hallmark of acute hypercapneic respiratory failure is elevated pCO2 due to retention/accumulation of carbon dioxide gas resulting in an acidic pH less than 7.35. There are many causes, but severe COPD is the most common.

The diagnosis is established by:

- **pCO2 greater than 50mmHg, and**
- **pH less than 7.35**

If the pH is normal (7.35–7.45) with elevated pCO2, the patient has chronic (not acute) respiratory failure.

Also, if the baseline is known, an increase in **pCO2 by 10mmHg or more indicates acute hypercapneic respiratory failure.** Finally, an **exacerbation of symptoms** requiring an increase in chronic supplemental oxygen indicates an "acute exacerbation" of chronic respiratory failure which would be classified as acute-on-chronic respiratory failure if properly documented.

Respiratory Acidosis: Physicians may diagnose acute hypercapneic respiratory failure as **"respiratory acidosis"** which is exactly the same thing. Unfortunately the code for "respiratory acidosis" is 276.2 which is a CC in contrast to the MCC status of acute respiratory failure, hence the need for clarification.

> **ICD-10**: *ICD-10 has codes for hypoxic and hypercapneic respiratory failure if documented by the physician, but they are not required. The MCC and CC status in ICD-9 does not change with ICD-10. For example, unspecified respiratory failure, unspecified whether with hypoxia or hypercapnia (J96.90) is still an MCC.*

Respiratory Failure following Surgery or Trauma (Codes 518.51–518.53)

The diagnosis of respiratory failure following surgery or trauma has regulatory and quality of care implications. It includes any cases of respiratory failure, ARDS, "shock lung" and "pulmonary insufficiency" that occur after surgery or trauma unless clearly specified as due to some other condition.

These diagnoses are classified as some of the most severe, life-threatening, reportable surgical complications a patient can have, and adversely affect quality scores for both the hospital and the surgeon. On the other hand, the diagnosis and coding of respiratory failure following surgery or trauma (an MCC) often results in a large payment increase to the hospital.

If improperly diagnosed without firm clinical grounds, it may become the basis for regulatory or contractual audits, penalties, or sanctions affecting the hospital and the physician. It has become a lucrative RAC target. Each hospital should have a policy that governs the coding of any condition (including respiratory failure) not supported by clinical criteria in the medical record.

To validate the diagnosis, the patient must have acute pulmonary dysfunction requiring non-routine aggressive measures. A patient who requires a short period of ventilatory support during surgical recovery does not have acute respiratory failure, and a code for it should not be assigned on the claim. The same is true for any duration of mechanical ventilation that is usual or expected following the type of surgery performed, unless there truly is underlying acute pulmonary dysfunction.

A further difficulty arises because most physicians consider "pulmonary insufficiency" to be a minor, clinically innocuous condition, not realizing its serious implications. To avoid confusion and improper code assignment, physicians should not use such a term in the post-operative setting unless the patient actually has acute severe pulmonary dysfunction.

RESPIRATORY FAILURE—ACUTE

ICD-10: *Codes for these conditions are located in Intraoperative and Postprocedural Complications and Disorders of Respiratory System, NEC (J95), and are MCCs:*

- *J95.1 Acute pulmonary insufficiency following thoracic surgery*
- *J95.2 Acute pulmonary insufficiency following nonthoracic surgery*
- *J95.3 Chronic pulmonary insufficiency following surgery*
- *J95.81 Postprocedural respiratory failure*

Chronic respiratory failure is very common in patients with severe COPD and other chronic lung diseases such as cystic fibrosis and pulmonary fibrosis. It is characterized by a combination of:

- Hypoxemia of variable severity (often with baseline pO2 < 60 mmHg on room air),
- Elevated pCO2,
- Elevated bicarbonate level (reported on ABG or basic metabolic panel),
- Normal pH (7.35–7.45)

The most important tip-off to chronic respiratory failure is chronic dependence on supplemental oxygen ("home O2"). Patients who qualify for home O2 almost always have chronic respiratory failure and a baseline pO2 < 60 mmHg. Another clue is finding an elevated bicarbonate level on the basic metabolic panel (BMP) in a COPD patient.

Example: A patient is admitted with CHF exacerbation and a history of severe COPD. ABG on room air shows pH 7.40, pCO_2 52 mmHg and pO_2 70 mmHg; bicarbonate level on BMP is elevated at 42. This is classic chronic respiratory failure: normal pH, elevated pCO_2 and bicarbonate, with some degree of hypoxemia – but no acute criteria.

Acute-on-Chronic Respiratory Failure

Definition: An acute exacerbation or decompensation of chronic respiratory failure. It is recognized by any of the following criteria:

- Worsening symptoms (usually with a need for increased supplemental oxygen), and/or
- Greater hypoxemia (decreasing pO2 from baseline), and/or
- Increased pCO2 with pH < 7.35.

RESPIRATORY FAILURE—CHRONIC

For patients treated with home O2, the pO2/SpO2 criteria can be applied, not on room air, but while receiving their usual supplemental oxygen flow. Home O2 is adjusted to maintain a pO2 > 60 mmHg (SpO2 > 91%). Therefore, if the pO2 has dropped below 60 mmHg (or SpO2 < 91%) on the usual supplemental oxygen flow rate, they now have acutely decompensated respiratory failure. Also in this situation patients may have already increased their home O2 on their own due to increasing hypoxemia with difficulty breathing indicative of an acute decompensation.

The P/F ratio should not be used to diagnose acute-on-chronic respiratory failure since many patients with chronic respiratory failure already have a P/F ratio < 300 (pO2 < 60 mmHg) on room air in their baseline stable state. That's the reason they are treated with chronic supplemental home oxygen in the first place.

Chronic Obst. Pulm. disease;

= COPD
chronic obs. bronchitis
Chronic bronchitis c̄ airway obst.
chronic bronchitis c̄ emphysema
chronic obst. tracheobronchitis

Document COPD separately from Asthma.

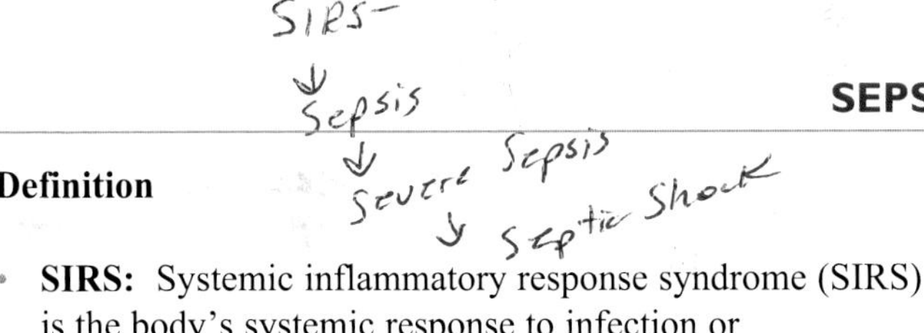

Definition

- **SIRS:** Systemic inflammatory response syndrome (SIRS) is the body's systemic response to infection or non-infectious causes such as trauma, burns, pancreatitis, major surgery, or other insult/injury.

- **Sepsis:** SIRS due to an infection (either suspected or confirmed). Excludes SIRS due to other causes.

- **Noninfectious SIRS:** SIRS due to causes other than infection.

Diagnostic Criteria for Sepsis

Sepsis is defined as SIRS due to an infection (either suspected or confirmed) as manifested by **two or more** of the following:

- **Fever** (≥ 101°F / > 38.3°C) or **Hypothermia** (< 96.8°F / < 36.0°C)
- **WBC** > 12,000 or < 4,000 or Bands > 10%
- **Lactate** > 2.0 mmol/L (> 4.0 is equivalent to septic shock)
- **Tachycardia** (pulse > 90)
- **Tachypnea** (respiratory rate > 20)
- Procalcitonin elevated
- C-reactive protein elevated
- Altered mental status
- Mottling of the skin or prolonged capillary refill
- Non-diabetic hyperglycemia (blood sugar > 120mg/dl)
- Other evidence of acute organ failure (severe sepsis)

The diagnosis of sepsis depends entirely on the physician's clinical interpretation of these criteria and their significance.

The consensus guidelines also recommend that, if any of these findings can, in the physician's judgment, be **"easily explained" by another coexisting condition** (other than the underlying infection), it should be excluded by the physician when deciding whether the patient has sepsis.

While not a specific requirement for the diagnosis, a patient with sepsis ought to be ill-appearing in some manner, but would not have to be specifically described as "septic" or "toxic."

In most circumstances, an underlying "localized" infection such as pneumonia, cellulitis, UTI, cholecystitis, diverticulitis, etc., can eventually be confirmed. However, it is not unusual to see cases of sepsis where a localized infection is not identified, particularly in immune-compromised patients or those on chemotherapy.

Guidance for Applying the Sepsis Criteria

- The first five criteria are commonly given the greatest weight but any and all of these may be used by physicians to establish a diagnosis of sepsis based on their clinical judgment. The more indicators a patient has, the more certain the diagnosis will be.
- Because tachypnea and tachycardia are so common in hospitalized patients for many reasons, they should not ordinarily be used as the only two criteria for diagnosing sepsis.
- The temperature (fever or hypothermia) and/or WBC criteria very strongly support the diagnosis of sepsis. Elevated lactate level and persistent hypotension are also particularly significant suggesting actual or impending severe sepsis.
- As stated by the sepsis guidelines: "Findings indicative of early organ dysfunction may be the first symptoms noted…"

- Contrary to a commonly held misconception, a positive blood culture is not a diagnostic criterion, although bacteremia (positive blood culture) would certainly be very strongly suggestive or confirmatory evidence.

References:

Crit Care Med 2013; 41: 580–637.
Crit Care Med 2008; 36: 296–327.
Crit Care Med 2003; 31: 250–1256.

Treatment may include IV antibiotics (often broad-spectrum, multiple), aggressive IV fluids to prevent organ failure, supplemental oxygen, careful monitoring of vital signs and organ function, and often intensive care.

Severe Sepsis

Section I.C.1.b of the Official Coding Guidelines (OCG) states: "Severe Sepsis [SIRS] generally refers to sepsis with associated acute organ dysfunction. If … the medical record documentation indicates that the acute organ dysfunction is related to a medical condition other than sepsis, do not assign code 995.92, severe sepsis. If the documentation is not clear …, query the provider."

Notice that the guidelines do not require specification of organ dysfunction "as due to" sepsis, which is assumed when "associated" with it unless another condition appears to be the cause.

The ICD-9-CM Tabular List enumerates several examples of acute organ dysfunction under code 995.92, using the words "such as," which means that the list is not all-inclusive. When these conditions represent a manifestation of severe sepsis, code 995.92 as well as the manifestations must be sequenced as secondary diagnoses.

Acute Organ Dysfunction: Conditions and clinical indicators of acute organ dysfunction that may be associated with severe sepsis include:

- Septic shock: Refractory hypotension (systolic blood pressure < 90mmHg, or mean arterial pressure < 60 mmHg, or reduction in systolic blood pressure of > 40 mmHg or more from baseline) associated with sepsis refractory to aggressive volume replacement and often requiring vasopressor therapy (such as Dopamine)
- Hyperlactatemia: Lactate level > 4 mmol/L which has the same severity and clinical implications as septic shock
- Hypoxemia/respiratory failure: P/F ratio < 300
- Acute kidney injury/renal failure or oliguria (falling urine output)
- Encephalopathy
- Coagulopathy or DIC: INR > 1.5, PTT > 60 seconds, platelets < 100,000
- Hyperbilirubinemia: Total bilirubin > 4 mg/dl
- Ileus (absent bowel sounds)
- Critical-illness myopathy
- Critical-illness polyneuropathy

Coding Guidelines for Sepsis

ICD-9-CM and Official Coding Guidelines indicate that sepsis is coded with a minimum of two codes:

1. Sequence first the systemic infection (038.9, 112.5, etc.)
2. Code also the appropriate SIRS code (995.91 or 995.92)

An additional code (not sequenced first) is also assigned for any localized infection(s) and associated manifestations of acute organ dysfunction if present (OCG I.C.1.b.1.b). Codes 995.91 or 995.92 are never sequenced as principal diagnosis.

Sequencing of sepsis with a localized infection: OCG assumes the relationship and requires sepsis be sequenced first.

OCG I.C.1.b.2.a: "If sepsis or severe sepsis is present on admission, and meets the definition of principal diagnosis, the systemic infection code (e.g., 038.xx, 112.5, etc) should be assigned as the principal diagnosis ..... A code should also be assigned [as a secondary diagnosis] for any localized infection, if present."

OCG I.C.1.b.3: "If the reason for admission is both sepsis, severe sepsis, or SIRS and a localized infection, such as pneumonia or cellulitis, a code for the systemic infection (038.xx, 112.5, etc) should be assigned first, then code 995.91 or 995.92, followed by the code for the localized infection..."

Based on OCG II.B & C (Two or more diagnoses that equally meet the definition for principal diagnosis), sepsis and an underlying infection cannot be considered co-equal because the OCG and ICD-9-CM Tabular List provide sequencing instructions.

When Sepsis is Not Principal Diagnosis: Circumstances identified by the OCG in which sepsis is not principal diagnosis include:

- Sepsis or the signs/symptoms of sepsis not present on admission.
- Sepsis as a complication of care (such as sepsis caused by a device or specifically documented as due to a procedure) in which case a complication code is sequenced first.
- Sepsis (even though present on admission) was not the principal reason for admission (did not meet the definition of principal diagnosis).

SEPSIS

Sepsis as a Complication: Sepsis is frequently due to the presence of a urinary catheter or vascular device, and in such situations, should be coded to the appropriate complication codes (categories 996–999), which would be sequenced first. For non-obstetrical post-procedural sepsis, complication code 998.59 is assigned first.

Urosepsis: If only the nonspecific term "urosepsis" is used, the physician should be queried to determine whether this is a simple UTI or sepsis due to the urinary tract infection. If only the term "urosepsis" is documented, then code 599.0 (urinary tract infection) is assigned.

Bacteremia: "Bacteremia" is defined as bacteria in the blood, i.e., a positive blood culture. It does not constitute sepsis and, as a Chapter 16 code (790.7), should rarely be assigned. When sepsis and bacteremia are both documented, it is not necessary to query for clarification since bacteremia is a symptom intrinsic to the diagnosis of sepsis.

Sepsis Syndrome: Although physicians generally use this term to mean "sepsis", *Coding Clinic* 2012, Second Quarter, p. 21 advises that, if only "sepsis syndrome" is documented, the physician should be queried to determine the specific condition(s) the patient has.

ICD-10: *Sepsis is coded with only code (A41.9 is for unspecified sepsis). Severe sepsis requires a code for sepsis (A41.9), followed by the code for severe sepsis (R65.20), with an additional code to identify the specific acute organ dysfunction.*

"Sepsis" must be specifically diagnosed since there is no code for "SIRS due to infection" as in ICD-9. ICD-10 has no code for "urosepsis" and provider must be queried.

Non-Infectious SIRS

Defined as SIRS due to causes other than infection. SIRS is caused by many conditions other than infection, such as pancreatitis, advanced malignancy, post-chemotherapy tumor lysis, extensive burns, major trauma, major surgical procedures, and bowel infarction (which may proceed to bacterial peritonitis, an infectious cause). The SIRS criteria are identical for all causes both infectious (sepsis) and noninfectious.

Physicians, even those who are familiar with the definition of sepsis as SIRS due to infection, often forget to document SIRS when its cause is noninfectious. A query for clarification is often needed.

For noninfectious SIRS, the underlying condition causing it is sequenced first, followed by the appropriate SIRS code:

- 995.93 without acute organ dysfunction (CC)
- 995.94 with acute organ dysfunction (MCC)

As with sepsis, SIRS codes are never assigned as principal diagnosis, but 995.93 is a CC and 995.94 is an MCC.

Pediatric Sepsis/SIRS

Definition: Pediatric SIRS in the presence of, or as a result of, suspected or proven infection.

The clinical criteria for pediatric sepsis/SIRS are quite different from the adult criteria and also depend upon the age of the patient (5th & 95th percentiles as specified in the reference below).

Continued —

SEPSIS

Pediatric SIRS/Sepsis Criteria (one must be temperature or WBC):

- Core temperature > 101.3° F/38.5° C or < 96.8° F/36.0° C
- WBC elevated or depressed for age (not due to chemotherapy) or > 10% bands
- Tachycardia (> 2 SD above normal for age not due to other stimuli), or
- Bradycardia (< 10th percentile for age not due to other specific causes), or
- Respiratory rate (> 2 SD above normal for age), or
- Mechanical ventilation (not due to anesthesia or neuromuscular disease)

Reference: Pediatr Crit Care Med 2005; 6(1): 2–8

TIA & PRECEREBRAL OCCLUSION/EMBOLISM

Definition of a TIA: A brief period of focal neurologic deficit lasting less than 24 hours (usually less than one hour) due to transiently blocked blood flow to a specific area of the brain.

Clinical Indicators of TIA:

- Neurologic symptoms resolve within 24 hours, and
- No acute infarction or hemorrhage on CT / MRI

Important: Persistence of a focal neurologic deficit >24 hours from onset is a stroke (CVA), not TIA. Duration is counted from onset, not presentation. Patients often present having already had symptoms for several hours or more.

The term "TIA" is problematic for documentation purposes. Physicians often use the term loosely as a specific diagnosis, but it is actually a symptom of a significant underlying cerebrovascular process. It's the underlying condition that really matters and is treated, not the symptom.

Diagnosis and Treatment of TIA

Diagnostic testing often includes trans-esophageal echocardiogram (TEE), carotid or trans-cranial Doppler, CT, MRI and occasionally MRA—all looking for sources of emboli, stenosis, occlusion or thrombosis.

Treatment includes anti-platelet therapy (such as aspirin, Persantin, Aggrenox, or Plavix) to prevent recurrent thrombosis or embolism, even when no significant abnormality is identified. Less often an anti-coagulant like Coumadin may be prescribed.

KR *See also Cerebrovascular Accident (CVA)*

Causes of TIA are the same as CVA

Almost every TIA is the result of:

1. **Stenosis** of a carotid, vertebral, or cerebral artery, or
2. **Thrombosis** at the site of stenosis or atherosclerotic plaque, or
3. **Cerebral embolism** originating from another location, such as carotid plaque or a fibrillating left atrium.

Stenosis of a cerebral or precerebral artery

Any degree of stenosis/narrowing of a carotid, vertebral or cerebral artery (even if "non-critical") is a possible cause of TIA due to transient reduction in blood flow, when it's location correlates clinically with the patient's symptoms. A lesion in a right-sided artery will cause symptoms on the left side of the body, and vice versa.

Many physicians hold the misimpression that the term **"non-critical" stenosis** (often reported on carotid Doppler or MRA studies) implies that the degree of stenosis is insignificant and not a potential source of cerebral embolism. This is clearly incorrect; any degree of stenosis can cause turbulent blood flow and may be the source of cerebral embolism resulting in a stroke or causing TIA.

"Non-critical" stenosis simply means that the degree of stenosis/narrowing of the artery in question is less than 50%–70% (depending upon the imaging technique and the presence of symptoms). It is "non-critical" because surgical intervention is not yet needed, and medical therapy to prevent further TIA or stroke will usually suffice.

Oddly for coding purposes, basilar / vertebral / vertebro-basilar *syndromes* are classified as TIA, unless specifically documented as occlusion, stenosis, embolism, narrowing, obstruction, thrombosis, stricture, or blockage of these arteries. A query is justified when only the "syndrome" is documented.

Thrombosis of a cerebral or precerebral artery

Localized thrombosis at the site of stenosis or atherosclerotic plaque may occur spontaneously obstructing blood flow to the brain. TIA results if the thrombus is transient and dissolves spontaneously as often happens; when prolonged a stroke is likely.

Transient Cerebral Embolism

Embolism of a small clot (typically composed primarily of platelets) to the brain from another location may obstruct blood flow causing a stroke or, if transient, TIA.

Common sources of transient cerebral **embolism** include:

- Atrial fibrillation – especially if PT/INR is subtherapeutic
- Valvular heart disease (aortic or mitral valves)
- Atrial septal defect (ASD) with "paradoxical embolus" of small clots from the right (venous) side of the heart across the ASD to the left heart and from there up to the brain
- Mural (ventricular wall) thrombus – especially following MI
- Any degree of stenosis / narrowing of a carotid, vertebral or cerebral artery

Even if nothing is found on evaluation to explain the TIA, the most likely cause of TIA is unexplained "transient cerebral embolism".

Coding and Documentation Issues

TIA as principal diagnosis is assigned to the non-specific, low-weighted DRG 69 TIA which has no CC or MCC options. The cerebral/precerebral stenosis, occlusions and cerebral embolism as causes of TIA are assigned to DRG 67–68 Nonspecific CVA & Precerebral Occlusion w/o Infarct with or without MCC.

Physicians should document the most likely, suspected or probable cause of the TIA, such as:

- "TIA, probably due to transient cerebral thromboembolism"
- "TIA, likely due to carotid stenosis"
- "TIA, suspect transient embolism due to atrial fibrillation"

Another diagnosis more specific than TIA (435.9) is "transient global ischemia" (437.7) assigned to DRG 70-72.

ICD-10: *No significant changes (category G45); unspecified TIA is code G45.9.*

Definition: A biopsy of the lung, not just the bronchus or endobronchial lesion, during endoscopic bronchoscopy, and used to diagnose lung neoplasm, sarcoidosis, interstitial fibrosis, or unexplained pulmonary infection or infiltrate.

Review all bronchoscopy procedure documentation carefully:

- Review the operative report and op note in detail for anything suggesting biopsy of the lung or lung tissue
- Look for lung tissue (alveoli) on the pathology report, which supports assignment of 33.27 per Coding Clinic, ThirdQuarter 2004, p. 9

However, the absence of lung tissue in the pathology report does not preclude the assignment of 33.27 when the procedure is performed and documented by the provider. Tissue samples may be inadequate or inconclusive (Coding Clinic, First Quarter 2011, p. 18; Third Quarter 2011, p. 6). This was further clarified in Coding Clinic, Third Quarter 2011, p. 7:

> "Code assignment is based on the providers report of what was actually done and not the pathology report. Small bits of lung tissue are seen from time to time on bronchoscopic biopsies. "

Do not confuse transbronchial biopsy with bronchial or endobronchial biopsy, brush biopsy, or bronchoalveolar lavage (33.24). Fine (Wang) needle aspiration/biopsy is coded 33.24 unless specified by physician as "transbronchial." (Coding Clinic, Second Quarter 2009, p. 16)

ICD-10: *Code assignment based on root operation excision and specific site of lung. For example: Excision, lower lung lobe, right, via natural or artificial opening endoscopic, diagnostic (0BBF8XZ)*

Little blue dot (mag. glass)
@ top of dx's:
Click it and will
bring up dx details
@ bottom of page

CMS has designated almost 1,600 diagnostic codes as MCCs, and more than 3,300 codes are CCs. For a complete list of the 2014 MCCs and CCs, go to the CMS website at *www.cms.gov/Medicare/Medicare-Fee-for-Service-Payment/AcuteInpatientPPS.*

As a practical reference, this section provides a listing of many of the most common MCCs and CCs and those that are often overlooked or not specifically documented by the physician. For each diagnosis, the key clinical criteria and indicators are identified to alert the user to the opportunities to query for and/or code these conditions.

To code these conditions as a secondary diagnosis, they must first **meet the definition of a secondary diagnosis.**

The definition of a secondary diagnosis is additional conditions (either present on admission or occurring during admission) that require any of the following:

- Clinical evaluation
- Therapeutic treatment
- Diagnostic procedures
- Increased nursing care/monitoring
- Extended length of stay

The criteria/indicators listed for each diagnosis are intended to be used as a guide only. The coding of a specific diagnosis should be evaluated on a case-by-case basis and based on physician documentation in the medical record.

ICD-10: *The secondary diagnosis coding guidelines are unchanged. The MCC/CC list when converted to ICD-10 has expanded but preserves the original list and is essentially unchanged.*

MCC-CC

Diagnosis	ICD-9	SI	ICD-10 *
Acute Coronary Insufficiency	41189	2	I24.8
Acute Coronary Occlusion	41181	2	I24.0
Acute Coronary Syndrome (ACS)	4111	2	I20.0
Acute Kidney Injury (AKI)	5849	3	N17.9
Acute Tubular Necrosis (ATN)	**5845**	**4**	**N17.0**
Anemia, Acute Blood Loss	2851	2	D62
Angina, Unstable	4111	2	I20.0
Aspiration Bronchitis	**5070**	**4**	**J69.0**
Atelectasis	5180	1	J98.11
Atrial Flutter	42732	1	I48.92
Anxiety, Alcohol induced	29189	1	F10.180
Bacteremia	7907	3	R78.81
Bipolar Disorder (Type I): Manic, depressed, or both	29640	1	F31.0
Bleeding, GI	5789	2	K92.2
Bleeding, Rectal / Anal	5693	1	K62.5
Blood in Stool (Melena)	5781	1	K92.1
BMI < 19	V850	1	Z68.1
BMI > 40 (not mcc)	**V8541**	**2**	**Z68.41**
Brain Death	**34882**	**4**	**G93.82**
C. Difficile Enteritis	00845	3	A04.7
Cachexia (cachetic)	7994	2	R64
CAD of Bypass Graft	41404	2	I25.810
Cancer, Metastatic	1970 -19889	2	C78.00- C79.89
Carcinomatosis	1990	2	C80.0
Cardiac Arrest (DC Alive)	**4275**	**4**	**I46.9**
Cellulitis/Abscess	6829	1	L03.90
Cellulitis, Leg	6826	2	L03.119

****MCCs are in bold**

Diagnosis	ICD-9	SI	ICD-10 *
Cerebral Edema	**3485**	**4**	**G93.6**
Cerebrovascular Accident (CVA)	**43491**	**4**	**I63.50**
Cerebral Hemorrhage	**431**	**4**	**I61.9**
CKD, Stage 4 & 5	5854, 5855	2	N18.4, N18.5
Coma	**78001**	**3**	**R40.20**
COPD, Acute Exacerbation	49121	2	J44.1
COPD, with Acute Bronchitis	49122	2	J44.0
Cor Pulmonale, Acute	**4150**	**4**	**I26.09**
Deep Vein Thrombosis (DVT)	4539	3	I82.91
Delirium, drug-induced	29281	2	F19.921
Demand Ischemia	41189	2	I24.8
Dementia, w Behavioral Disturbance	29411	2	F02.81
Dementia: Senile, Presenile, Vascular w delirium, delusion, or depression	29011 -29043	2	F03.91
Depression, Major / Acute Mild, Moderate, Recurrent	29621, 29622, 29630	2	F32.0, F32.1, F33.9
Depression, Major, Unspecified	29620	1	F32.9
Diabetes, Hyperosmolar with or without coma	**25020**	**4**	**E11.00 E11.01**
Diabetes, with Coma	**25030**	**4**	**E11.641**
Diabetes, with Ketoacidosis (Type I, Type II)	**25010**	**3**	**E10.10 E13.10**
Drug Dependence, continuous use	30491	1	F19.20
Emaciation / Emaciated	**261**	**4**	**E41**
Encephalopathy	**34830**	**3**	**G93.40**
Encephalopathy, Alcoholic	2912	2	F10.27

****MCCs are in bold**

MCC-CC

Diagnosis	ICD-9	SI	ICD-10 *
Encephalopathy, Anoxic, Hypoxic	3481	3	G93.1
Encephalopathy, Hypertensive	4372	3	I67.4
Encephalopathy, Metabolic	**34831**	**3**	**G93.41**
Encephalopathy, Toxic	**34982**	**3**	**G92**
Enteritis, Bacterial	0085	2	A04.9
Enteritis, C. diff	00845	3	A04.7
Enteritis, E. coli	00800	2	A04.4
Esophageal Ulcer	53020	2	K22.10
Esophageal Ulcer with bleeding	**53021**	**3**	**K22.11**
Esophagitis, Acute	53012	1	K20.9
Esophagitis, Candida	11284	2	B37.81
ESRD	**5856**	**2**	**N18.6**
Gastritis, Hemorrhagic	**53551**	**3**	**K29.71**
Hallucinations	7801	1	R44.3
Heart Failure: Diastolic	42830	2	I50.30
Heart Failure: Diastolic, Acute	**42831**	**3**	**I50.31**
Heart Failure: Left	4281	2	I50.1
Heart Failure: Systolic	42820	2	I50.20
Heart Failure: Systolic, Acute	**42821**	**3**	**I50.21**
Hematemesis	5780	3	K92.0
Hemiplegia / Hemiparesis	34290	2	G81.90
Hemiplegia / Hemiparesis s/p CVA	43820	2	I69.959
Hemoptysis	78630	2	R04.2
Hepatic Coma	**5722**	**4**	**K72.91**
Hepatic Encephalopathy	**5722**	**4**	K72.90
Hepatitis, Viral	0709	1	B19.9
HIV Disease / AIDS	**042**	**3**	**B20**
Hypernatremia	2760	3	E87.0

****MCCs are in bold**

Diagnosis	ICD-9	SI	ICD-10 *
Hypertension, accelerated	4010	2	I10
Hyponatremia	2761	2	E87.1
Ileus	5601	2	K56.7
Intestinal Impaction	56030	2	K56.49
Intestinal Obstruction	5609	3	K56.60
Malnutrition, Mild	2631	2	E44.1
Malnutrition, Severe	**261, 262**	**4**	**E41, E43**
Malnutrition: Moderate, other, unspecified	2630, 2638, 2639	3	E44.0 E46
Myocardial Infarction, Acute	**41091**	**4**	**I21.3**
Obesity Hypoventilation Syndrome	27803	2	E66.2
Pancreatic Cyst, Pseudocyst	5772	3	K86.2, K86.3
Pancreatitis, Acute	**5770**	**3**	**K85.9**
Pancreatitis, Chronic	5771	2	K86.1
Pancytopenia	28419	3	D61.818
Pancytopenia, due to chemo or drugs	**28411 28412**	**3**	**D61.810 D61.811**
Peritoneal Abscess	**56722**	**4**	**K65.1**
Peritonitis	**5679**	**3**	**K65.9**
Pneumonia	**486**	**3**	**J18.9**
Pneumonia, due to chemical, fumes, vapors	5060	2	J68.0
Pneumonia, post-procedural aspiration	99732	4	J95.89
Pneumonia, VAP	99731	3	J95.851
Pressure ulcer, Stage III	**70723**	**2**	**L89.93**
Pressure ulcer, Stage IV	**70724**	**3**	**L89.94**
PSVT / PAT	4270	2	I47.1
Quadriplegia, Functional	**78072**	**3**	**R53.2**

****MCCs are in bold**

MCC-CC

Diagnosis	ICD-9	SI	ICD-10 *
Respiratory Distress, Acute	51882	2	J80
Respiratory Failure: Acute / Unspecified	**51881**	**4**	**J96.90 J96.91**
Respiratory Failure: Acute on Chronic	**51884**	**4**	**J96.20**
Respiratory Failure: Following Surgery or Trauma	**51851**	**4**	**J95.821**
Respiratory Failure: Chronic	51883	3	J96.10
Schatzki's Ring	**7503**	**3**	**Q39.0**
Schizophrenia, chronic	29592	1	F20.9
Sepsis/SIRS	**0389**	**3**	**A41.9**
Shock	78550	4	R57.9
Shock: Cardiogenic Septic Hypovolemic	**78551 78552 78559**	**4**	**R57.0 R65.21 R57.1**
SIRS, Noninfectious	99593	2	R65.10
SIRS, Noninfectious with Organ Dysfunction	**99594**	**4**	**R65.11**
Suicidal Ideation	V62.84	2	R45.851
Thrombophlebitis / Phlebitis, Deep Veins	45119	3	I80.209
Thrombophlebitis and Phlebitis, following infusion	9992	2	T80.1XXA
Thrush, Oral	1120	2	B37.0
TIA (Transient Ischemic Attack)	4359	2	G45.9
Ulcer, Lower Limb	70710	2	L97.909
Urinary Tract Infection	5990	2	N39.0
Ventricular fibrillation (DC alive)	**42741**	**4**	**I49.01**
Ventricular Tachycardia	4271	3	I47.2

****MCCs are in bold**

Diagnosis	ICD-9	SI	ICD-10 *
Vertebral Compression Fracture: Non-traumatic (pathologic)	73313	2	M80.08XA
Vertebral Compression Fracture: Traumatic	8058	2	S32.009A

****MCCs are in bold**

*The ICD-10 codes listed do not include all codes available for the diagnosis, only the least specific code to meet MCC/CC status.

All ICD-10 codes remain a MCC or CC except those noted in red.

Non-CC Diagnoses with SI Level 2-3

Diagnosis	ICD-9	SI
Alzheimer's disease	3310	2
Anorexia	7830	2
Atrial fibrillation	42731	2
CHF	4280	2
Cirrhosis of Liver	5715	2
COPD	496	2
COPD with asthma	49320	2
Cor pulmonale, chronic	4169	2
Cystitis	5959	2
DM uncontrolled	25002	2
DM with renal, neuro, circulatory, other manifestions	250.40-250.93	2
Dysphagia	78720	2
Eating disorder	30750	2
Electrolyte/fluid disorder	2769	2
Emphysema	4928	2
Failure to thrive	7837	2
Head injury	95901	2
Hypercalcemia	27542	2
Hypocalcemia	27541	2
Hyperkalemia	2767	2
Hypotension	458.9	2
Jaundice	7804	2
Morbid obesity	27801	2
Multiple sclerosis	340	2
Myopathy	3599	2
Neutropenia	28800	3

Non-CC Diagnoses with SI Level 2-3

Diagnosis	ICD-9	SI
Nutritional deficiency	2699	2
Oliguria/anuria	7885	2
Parkinson's Disease	3320	2
Pressure ulcer, site NOS	70700	2
Pressure ulcer, Upper/lower back, hip, buttock	70702-70705	3
Renal calculus	5920	2
Seizure Disorder	78039	2
Shingles/Herpes Zoster	0539	2
Sick sinus syndrome	42781	2
Sickle cell disease	28260	2
Syncope	7802	2
Systemic lupus erythematosus	7100	2
Thrombocytopenia	287.5	2
Vitamin deficiency	2692	2
Vitamin D deficiency	2689	2

Diagnosis	Codes	SI	Clinical Criteria/Indicators
Acute Coronary Insufficiency Acute Coronary Occlusion KR	41189 41181	2	Coronary insufficiency or occlusions without AMI. If troponin elevated, clarify if NSTEMI. Includes "acute ischemic heart disease."
Acute Coronary Syndrome (ACS)	4111	2	Should be clarified during admission as either unstable angina or acute MI. Physicians often imply acute MI with this term, but only codes as 4111, unstable angina. When troponin elevated, clarify if NSTEMI. See KR Myocardial Ischemia.
Acute Kidney Injury (AKI) KR Acute Renal Failure (ARF)	5849	3	Criteria: (1) Increase creatinine by ≥ 0.3 within 48 hrs, or (2) Increase creatinine to 1.5x baseline or more within 7 days (confirmed duration or presumed), or (3) Decrease urine output < 0.5 cc/kg/hr x 6 hrs or more. Most common cause is dehydration.
Acute Tubular Necrosis (ATN) KR	**5845**	4	ATN is responsible for about one-third of inpatient cases of acute renal failure/acute kidney injury. Typically takes > 72 hours for creatinine to return toward baseline. Look for prolonged volume depletion, hypotension, sepsis, surgery, drug toxicity including vancomycin, gentamicin, NSAIDs. Urinary sodium concentration >40%; fractional excretion of sodium (FEIN) > 2%.

Diagnosis	Codes	SI	Clinical Criteria/Indicators
Anemia, Acute Blood Loss	2851	2	Key concept is development or worsening of anemia due to acute blood loss, not the amount of blood lost. Anemia is Hgb/Hct below normal range. If preexisting anemia, decrease Hgb/Hct by 1-2 gm/3-6% or symptoms is usually significant. Typically occurs after surgery, trauma, or due to GI bleeding. Transfusion supports diagnosis but is not required.
Angina, Unstable also called "acute coronary Syndrome"	4111	2	Angina in which the pattern of symptoms changes: increased severity, frequency, duration, or with less exertion, or during rest. Equivalent terms include accelerated, crescendo, pre-infarction, progressive angina. Look for no relief from up to 3 nitroglycerin tablets x 15-20 min, topical or IV NTG, transferred for cath or CABG. Elevated troponin may indicate progression beyond unstable angina to AMI especially NSTEMI.
Anxiety, Alcohol-Induced	29189	1	Look for anxiety with underlying alcohol abuse, dependence, withdrawal.
Aspiration Bronchitis	**5070**	4	Same risk factors as aspiration pneumonia (NH patient, recent vomiting, debilitated, dysphagia, history of CVA, alcoholism, NG tube), but patient develops bronchitis, not pneumonia.

Diagnosis	Codes	SI	Clinical Criteria/Indicators
Atelectasis clears promptly c̄ tx (infiltrate takes weeks)	5180	1	Collapse in some portion of lung; to be distinguished from pneumothorax (“collapsed lung”) with air between lung and chest wall. Sometimes a trivial finding on X-ray report (not coded). Other times significant clinical problem, particularly post-op, with increased risk of pneumonia, hypoxia. Look for clinical findings of fever, rales, chest x-ray positive for atelectasis. If significant, may require further workup, such as chest x-ray, lab, breathing exercises, incentive spirometry, respiratory therapy. Usually clears promptly on chest x-ray with treatment; distinguish from infiltrate which takes weeks to clear.
Atrial Flutter if ass. c̄ at. fib - code both	42732	1	Rapid, often regular heart beat; regular prominent P-waves (“saw-tooth”); atrial rate >240 often with variable AV-block resulting in slower and/or irregular ventricular rate/pulse. Almost always “acute” and symptomatic: palpitations, SOB, syncope, chest pain/tightness. Look for episodes of atrial flutter associated with atrial fibrillation; if both documented by a provider (e.g., “fib/flutter”), code both.

Diagnosis	Codes	SI	Clinical Criteria/Indicators
Bacteremia "positive blood culture"	7907	3	"Positive blood culture". Literally means "bacteria in the blood". Validate that the positive culture is not a "contaminant" (false positive). Qualifies for code assignment as an additional diagnosis (e.g., monitored and clinically evaluated). Since it is a "symptom" of sepsis, does not require clarification when both are diagnosed.
Bipolar Disorder, Type I Mild or moderate Severe	296x0 -296x3 296x4	1 1 2	Hereditary mood disorder characterized by alternating phases of highly variable depression and mania (occasionally psychosis); some cases manifest depression only; drug/alcohol abuse common; high rate of suicide; look for treatment with Lithium, Depakote, Tegretol, Lamictal, Risperdol, Abilify, others. Any degree of "remission" is not a CC.
Bleeding (Hemorrhage) Gastrointestinal (GI) Rectal / Anal Blood in stool (Melena)	 5789 5693 5781	 2 1 1	Almost any type of GI bleeding is significant. Melena = black tarry stools = digested blood usually due to UGI bleeding. Hematochezia = bright red rectal bleeding usually due to lower GI bleeding (colon, rectum, anal). Anal or rectal bleeding (not due to hemorrhoids) = 5693. Not simply positive occult blood test (7921)

Diagnosis	Codes	SI	Clinical Criteria/Indicators
BMI < 19	V850	1	BMI may be documented by non-physician like nutritionist or nurse, but needs corresponding clinical condition (underweight, anorexia, malnourished, etc.) documented by MD. If BMI <16, look for other clinical indicators for "severe" malnutrition which is an MCC.
BMI ≥ 40	V8541-V8545	2	BMI may be documented by non-physician like nutritionist or nurse, but needs corresponding clinical condition (obesity, morbid obesity, overweight, etc.) documented by MD.
Brain Death	**34882**	4	Total, or almost total, cessation of brain function. "Flat" EEG, no clinical neurologic function.
C. Difficile Enteritis	00845	3	Commonly associated with recent antibiotic therapy, especially broad-spectrum. Highly-contagious: NH status or recent hospitalization. Stool test for C. diff identifies the toxin, not the organism. Usually treated with Flagyl.
Cachexia (cachetic)	7994	2	Usually indicated in the physical exam; clinically may imply severely malnourished, muscle wasting / atrophy; most often associated with malignancy.

Diagnosis	Codes	SI	Clinical Criteria/Indicators
CAD of Bypass Graft (not native artery)	41402 41403 41404	2	Coronary artery disease or atherosclerosis of bypass graft (not native artery). Includes autologous and non-autologous vein grafts or an arterial graft (such as radial or internal mammary), but not unspecified type of graft - 41405. May be mentioned if cannot be revascularized.
Cancer, Metastatic	1970 - 19889	2	Review past medical history and/or pathology report for any metastatic sites, such as bone, lymph nodes, brain, liver, peritoneum.
Carcinomatosis	1990	2	Widespread dissemination of cancer (carcinoma) throughout the body. If the physician lists the metastatic sites, all sites should be coded individually. If the physician documents the diagnosis of carcinomatosis without mention of specific sites, assign this code. *Coding Clinic* 1989 Q4 P10.
Cardiac Arrest (DC Alive)	**4275**	4	Often a terminal/fatal event associated with ventricular arrhythmia, complete heart block, asystole, respiratory failure/ arrest. MCC if pt is resuscitated and dc'd alive. Common with AMI, massive blood loss, severe CHF, severe electrolyte imbalance and certain drug toxicity, poisoning, drug overdose.

Diagnosis	Codes	SI	Clinical Criteria/Indicators
Cellulitis/Abscess Cellulitis/Abscess, Leg	6820-6825, 6827-6829 6826	1 2	Look for skin or wound infection, cutaneous ulcer or wound with associated cellulitis. Skin redness, swelling, heat, tenderness, fever, elevated WBC. Look for clinical indicators for sepsis.
Cerebral Edema	**3485**	4	Requires clinically significant or generalized brain swelling / edema documented by provider, not just minor localized edema surrounding a lesion noted on CT or MRI. Especially with CVA, neoplasm or trauma. Usually requires treatment with high-dose IV steroids.
Cerebrovascular Accident (CVA) KR MRI – acute infarct or hemorrhage	**43491**	4	Persistence of focal neurologic deficit ≥ 24 hours indicates CVA regardless of CT/MRI findings. Usually principal diagnosis. MRI is best test and will usually identify acute infarct or hemorrhage. CT will identify hemorrhage but acute infarct often not visualized for several days.
Cerebral Hemorrhage	**430, 431, 432x**	4	Hemorrhagic stroke, ruptured cerebral aneurysm, hypertensive hemorrhage; check imaging studies. Most subdural and epidural hemorrhage are traumatic.

Diagnosis	Codes	SI	Clinical Criteria/Indicators
CKD, Stage 4 & 5 KR	5854, 5855	2	Chronic Kidney Disease stages are based on the GFR: Stage 4 = GFR 15-29, Stage 5 = GFR < 15.
Coma	**78001**	3	Profound alteration of mental status ranging from severe obtundation with impaired responsiveness, to unconsciousness with some responsiveness, to complete unresponsiveness. Causes include head trauma, acute cerebrovascular disease, etc. The Glasgow Coma Scale (GCS) 3-8 for severe brain injury corresponds to coma. ICD-10: Some Coma Scale response scores are MCCs: motor, verbal, eye-opening.
COPD, Acute Exacerbation COPD, with Acute Bronchitis	49121 49122	2	Indicators of "acute" status are worsening symptoms, hypoxia or increased home O2 flow rate. Often co-exists/co-equal with respiratory failure, pneumonia, heart failure. Sequencing of principal diagnosis depends on circumstances. The terms "exacerbation" or "decompensated" = "acute exacerbation."

Diagnosis	Codes	SI	Clinical Criteria/Indicators
Cor Pulmonale, Acute	**4150**	4	Very common with acute exacerbation of COPD or pulmonary embolism. Defined as acute right-sided heart failure or "acute pulmonary heart disease" (also 4150) caused by pulmonary hypertension. Comparable to acute systolic / diastolic [right] heart failure; usually diastolic in nature. Echo shows pulmonary hypertension and/or acute right ventricular strain/failure/ dysfunction. Distinguish from chronic (4169) which is non-CC.
Deep Vein Thrombosis (DVT)	45340-45341 45382-4539 45342-45381	3	Superficial or deep, acute or chronic, almost any location. Unilateral leg/arm swelling with or without pain; immobility, recent surgery (especially hip, knee, lower extremity), cancer, mastectomy, recent travel. DVT with inflammation = see Thrombophlebitis and Phlebitis.
Delirium, drug induced	29281	2	Clinically the same as toxic encephalopathy (MCC). Agitation, confusion, disorientation, combativeness, and/or hallucinations. Unspecified "delirium" is non-CC; clarify if possibly drug-induced or if encephalopathy.
Demand Ischemia	41189	2	Acute myocardial ischemia (with or without chest pain) primarily caused by CAD but due to other cardiac stress such as hypoxia, rapid arrhythmia, hypotension, severe anemia or acute blood loss. Troponin often elevated without MI, but may progress to MI especially if EKG changes.

Diagnosis	Codes	SI	Clinical Criteria/Indicators
Dementia with Behavioral Disturbance Ex. Alzheimers Parkinson's	29421	2	Look for documentation or indications of Alzheimer's, Parkinsons, or other types of dementia with behavioral disturbances including: aggressive, combative, violent behavior, wandering off.
Dementia: Senile, Presenile or Vascular/Arteriosclerotic with: Delirium (acute confusion) Delusions Depressive	29011-29041	2	Must be specified as senile, presenile or vascular/arteriosclerotic (multi-infarct dementia) associated with delirium, delusions, depression (specific linkage as "due to' not required). ICD-10: Unspecified dementia includes senile & presenile (F0391), Vascular dementia with behavior disturbance (F0151), Delirium with dementia (F05).
Depression, Major (MDD): Single or recurrent episode; Unspecified/Mild/ Moderate/ Severe/ Psychotic	 29620 29621 29624	 1 2 3	Symptoms may include insomnia, anorexia, withdrawn, moody, sadness, suicidal thought; often chronic, recurrent, but can result from single traumatic emotional event. Look for Psych consult; medication adjustment; documentation of depression with acute state, acute confusion, delirium or hallucinations. Unspecified "depression" (311) is non-CC. ICD-10: Major depression, unspecified (29620), will no longer be a CC.

Diagnosis	Codes	SI	Clinical Criteria/Indicators
Diabetes, with **Ketoacidosis** **Hyperosmolar** **Coma**	 **25010-25013** **24910-24911** **25030-25033** **24930-24931**	3 4	Look for documentation of coma, ketoacidosis, hyperosmolar state including diabetes with pH < 7.35 (acidosis), positive test for serum ketones (ketosis), hypernatremia, and even normal serum sodium level with hyperglycemia (= hyperosmolar state). ICD-10: Type II DM with ketoacidosis should be coded to E13.10 (not E11.69) for MCC (per CC 2013 Q3, p. 26).
Drug Dependence, continuous use (not alcohol)	30491	1	Dependence means withdrawal syndrome likely if drug use stopped. Continuous use means daily or almost daily use. Distinguish from "episodic" use. Applies not just to abuse and maintenance drug (e.g. methadone) but also therapeutic use with dependence (e.g. cancer or chronic pain syndrome). May document specific medication such as Fentayl, morphine or hydrocodone dependence to avoid stigma of "drug". Does not include alcohol. ICD-10: Drug dependence, unspecified = CC.
Emaciation / Emaciated	**261**	4	Wasted condition of the body due to disease or lack of nutrition. Equivalent to severe malnutrition (261) but *Coding Clinic* First Quarter 2013, page 13 indicates malnutrition must be diagnosed or defaults to cachexia (7994).

Diagnosis	Codes	SI	Clinical Criteria/Indicators
Encephalopathy (KR) - underlying systemic cause - Reversible when cause is corrected	**34830, 34839**	3	Acute generalized alteration in mental function (communication, memory, speech, orientation, behavior) due to an underlying systemic cause reversible when the cause is corrected. Often classified as metabolic or toxic, but may be unspecified. Most inpatients with acutely altered mental status have an encephalopathy as the cause.
Encephalopathy - Alcoholic	2912	2	Chronic in nature, typically due to thiamine deficiency. Specific types are Wernicke's and Korsakoff's encephalopathy.
Encephalopathy - Anoxic, Hypoxic	3481	3	Chronic due to anoxic brain damage.
Encephalopathy - Hypertensive	4372	3	An acute or subacute consequence of severe hypertension marked by headache, obtundation, confusion, or stupor, with or without convulsions. Papilledema may be noted.
Encephalopathy (KR) **Metabolic, Toxic**	**34831, 34982**	3	Causes include infection, fever, sepsis, dehydration, acidosis, electrolyte imbalance, hypoxia, organ failure, poisoning, toxins, drug-induced.

Diagnosis	Codes	SI	Clinical Criteria/Indicators
Enteritis, Bacterial	0085	2	Look for antibiotic treatment in cases of colitis, enteritis, gastroenteritis. May indicate possible C. diff or E. coli or other bacteria.
Enteritis, C. diff	00845	3	Clostridium difficile (C. diff). Commonly associated with recent antibiotic therapy, especially broad-spectrum. Highly-contagious: nursing home status or recent hospitalization. Stool test for C. diff identifies the toxin, not the organism. Usually treated with Flagyl.
Enteritis, E. coli	00800	2	Inflammation of small intestine due to E. coli; common form of traveler's diarrhea. In some cases E. coli can produce a toxin similar to C. diff. which may be potentially life-threatening.
Esophagitis Acute Candida	 53012 11284	 1 2	Acute esophagitis (53012) and esophagitis due to Candida. Usually found on EGD. ICD-10: "Acute" esophagitis no longer a CC.
Esophageal Ulcer (Erosions codes to ulcers)	53020	2	Esophageal ulcerations without bleeding (53020). Check endoscopy report - ulcerations, erosions. ICD-10: Esophageal "erosions" codes to "ulcers" and will be a CC.

Diagnosis	Codes	SI	Clinical Criteria/Indicators
Esophageal Ulcer with bleeding	**53021**	3	Usually found on EGD - ulcerations, erosions. ICD-10: Esophageal “erosions” codes to “ulcers” and with bleeding will be MCC.
ESRD	**5856**	2	Chronic kidney disease Stage 5 requiring chronic dialysis (dialysis-dependent).
Gastritis, Hemorrhagic	**53551**	3	Any form of gastritis documented with hemorrhage including acute, chronic, atrophic, alcoholic, hypertrophic, bile-induced, superficial, toxic, allergic, unspecified, duodenitis, and gastroduodenitis. Check endoscopy report.
Hallucinations	7801	1	Includes auditory or olfactory (7801), and due drug (29212) or alcohol (2913), but not visual (36816)
Heart Failure: Diastolic KR	42830 42832	2	Hypertrophic ventricle, strong contraction; small ventricular chamber; ventricle does not relax properly; impaired filling with blood. EF is normal (55-70%) or elevated on echocardiogram. Common cause is HTN or ESRD. “Diastolic” must be documented.
Heart Failure: Systolic KR	42820 42822	2	Dilated, weak heart. Ejection fraction (EF) < 40% on echocardiogram is diagnostic. Common cause is CAD/ischemia. “Systolic” must be documented. If acute = MCC.

Diagnosis	Codes	SI	Clinical Criteria/Indicators
Heart Failure: Systolic or Diastolic, Acute	**42821, 42823 42831, 42833 42841, 42843**	3	"Acute" heart failure specified as systolic, diastolic or combined. Indicators of an acute state: IV medications; supplemental oxygen required; pulmonary edema / congestion or increasing pleural effusions on CXR; exacerbation of symptoms, difficulty breathing, swelling of extremities; BNP > 500 / Pro-BNP >3000. The terms "decompensated" or "exacerbation" = "acute".
Heart Failure: Left	4281	2	Left-sided heart failure may lead to fluid accumulation in the lungs. May imply systolic heart failure. This code is not classified as acute or chronic – no MCC option unless further specified as "systolic/diastolic" and "acute".
Hematemesis	5780	3	Hematemesis: Vomiting blood; quantity not specified: may be mild or massive.
Hemiplegia / Hemiparesis	43820-43822 34200-34292	2	Paralysis or weakness in one-side body (arm and/or leg), usually result of stroke (acute or residual "late effect"). Need to clarify if documented as right or left sided "weakness." I-10: Category I69 specified to cause (e.g., following cerebral infarction) and dominant, non-dominant, unspecified side.
Hemoptysis	78630 78639	2 1	Literally "coughing up blood." May be massive or only blood-tinged. A symptom code that can qualify as a secondary diagnosis if not integral to underlying condition or if further evaluation needed.

Diagnosis	Codes	SI	Clinical Criteria/Indicators
Hepatic Coma	**5722**	4	Coma due to cirrhosis/liver failure. Often principal reason for admission in patients with cirrhosis. Look for treatment with lactulose. See Coma, Hepatic Encephalopathy.
Hepatic Encephalopathy	**5722**	4	Altered mental staus due to cirrhosis/liver failure. Often principal reason for admission in patients with cirrhosis. Look for treatment with lactulose. ICD-10: Non-CC unless specified with coma.
Hepatitis, Viral MCC if c coma	0709	1	Viral hepatitis without coma, unspecified or specified as Type A, B, E or delta - acute or chronic. Type C acute only. MCC if with coma.
HIV Disease / AIDS KR	**042**	3	Any patient with a known prior diagnosis of AIDS or an HIV-related condition should be coded to 042. Once a patient has developed an HIV-related illness/AIDS, code 042 must always be assigned on every subsequent admission. Patients previously diagnosed with AIDS or any HIV illness (042) should never again be assigned to code V08 (asymptomatic HIV infection). Code V08 is for HIV-positive only without AIDS.

Diagnosis	Codes	SI	Clinical Criteria/Indicators
Hypernatremia >145 code includes dehydration Tx D5 ½ NS	2760	3	Serum sodium >145; often with dehydration; treatment with hypotonic IVF (e.g., D5 ½ NS). Code includes "dehydration" (not separately coded when 2760 assigned).
Hypertension, accelerated	4010	2	Systolic BP >180 or diastolic BP >110. Key factor is urgent treatment. May be described as "severe", "uncontrolled", "crisis", "urgent", "emergent", but the term "accelerated" (or "malignant") must be documented for correct code assignment. Urgent treatment = clonidine, lopressor, hydralazine, and IV-infusion of nitroprusside or nitroglycerin. ICD-10: Code I10 - Hypertension (no specificity) is no longer a CC.
Hyponatremia <135	2761	2	Sodium level <135; often diuretic-induced. Look for serum/urine osmolality. Treatment is fluid restriction, withhold diuretics, and (if severe) sodium infusion. Sometimes due to SIADH (2536) = CC.
Ileus Intestinal Obstruction common 3-4 days postop GI surgery	5601 5609	2 3	Needs to be a significant clinical problem, not just a finding on X-ray report. Findings may include decreased bowel sounds, no BM, abdominal pain/distention, NG tube. Ileus commonly occurs following surgery and may last up to 3-4 days after GI surgery. Also, look for "ileus" accompanying other GI disorders. Not a complication of care unless prolonged/unexpected.

Diagnosis	Codes	SI	Clinical Criteria/Indicators
Intestinal Impaction	56030 56039	2	Associated with fecal impaction, review abdominal xray or CT for intestinal, colon, rectosigmoid impaction.
Malnutrition: Mild, Moderate, Other, Unspecified KR	2631 2630, 2638, 2639	2 3	Albumin level usually < 3.0 gm/dl, weight loss, cancer, BMI < 18.5, malabsorption syndromes, end-stage disease processes. See nutritionist consults.
Malnutrition: Severe KR	**261, 262** emaciated	4	Severe muscle atrophy, BMI <16, Albumin < 2.0, severe weight loss. Cancer is common cause. "Emaciated" (261) is equivalent term. See nutrition consults. If "cachexia/ cachectic" (7994 = CC) documented, clarify if actually severe malnutrition (MCC).
Myocardial Infarction, Acute KR	**41091**	4	Increased Troponin. "Acute" = onset 8 weeks or less. Clarify if AMI if "acute coronary syndrome" is documented. NSTEMI = "subendocardial" infarction; STEMI = "transmural" infarction. I-10: Acute onset 4 weeks or less with continued treatment = Acute MI.
Obesity Hypoventilation Syndrome Pickwickian Syndrome	27803	2	Synonym = Pickwickian Syndrome. Condition in which poor breathing due to obesity leads to lower O2 levels and higher CO2 levels in the blood causing inadequate sleep and daytime somnolence. Most patients also have a form of sleep apnea.

Diagnosis	Codes	SI	Clinical Criteria/Indicators
Pancreatitis, Acute (chronic - cc)	**5770**	3	Abdominal, back, flank pain; fever, nausea, vomiting. Increased Amylase, Lipase, IV antibiotics, NG-suction. Tends to be recurrent; often related to alcohol or common bile duct stone. Distinguish from chronic (5771) which is a CC.
Pancreatitis, Chronic Pancreatic Cyst or Pseudocyst	5771 5772	2 3	Alcoholism; hypertriglyceridemia; diabetes; prior pancreatitis or pancreatic surgery; frequently recurrent. Amylase sometimes normal; lipase elevated (more sensitive and specific). Chronic pain meds and/or enzyme replacement therapy (e.g., Creon, Pancrease, Viokase, Zenpep) are common treatments for chronic pancreatitis.
Pancytopenia	28419	3	Reduction in the number of red blood cells (anemia), white blood cells (neutropenia) and platelets (thrombocytopenia). Neutropenia = less than 1500 neutrophils (ANC); thrombocytopemia < 100,000; anemia = below lower range of normal. Check WBC and platelets in patients with anemia.
Pancytopenia **Due to chemotherapy** **Due to drugs**	 **28411** **28412**	 3	Pancytopenia when caused by chemotherapy or other drugs. Check WBC and platelets in patients with anemia.

Diagnosis	Codes	SI	Clinical Criteria/Indicators
Peritoneal Abscess **Peritonitis**	**56722** **5679**	4 3	Inflammation, usualy implying infection, of the peritoneum lining intra-abdominal organs. Significant peritonitis often occurs with intra-abdominal infections such as appendicitis, diverticulitis, bowel perforation or abscess. Physical exam: abdominal rigidity or rebound tenderness. CT scan: fluid accumulation or description of peritonitis. Operative findings: exudates, purulence, pus, serositis.
Pneumonia (need infiltrate on chest X-Ray or CT	**486**	3	Most forms of pneumonia as a secondary diagnosis (whether present on admission or occurring after admission) qualify as an MCC. Usually need infiltrate on chest x-ray or CT scan, or an explanation by provider to substantiate diagnosis.
Pneumonia, due to chemical, fumes, vapors	5060	2	Often documented as "pneumonitis". Clarify cause.
Pneumonia VAP Post-procedural aspiration	 99731 99732	 3 4	Pneumonia attributable to mechanical ventilation or ventilator-associated (99731) or documented as aspiration complicating a procedure or surgery (99732). Code 997.31 is assigned only when the pneumonia is specifically documented as ventilator-associated – not just a pneumonia occurring in a ventilated patient.

Diagnosis	Codes	SI	Clinical Criteria/Indicators
Pressure (Decubitus) Ulcer **Stage III** KR **Stage IV**	 **70723** **70724**	 2 3	Common in nursing home patients. Look for skin wound or ulcer in nursing notes and wound care services. Provider must specify diagnosis and POA status, non-physician may document stage. Check for any excisional debridement.
PSVT / PAT plain SVT- not cc	4270	2	Documentation of PSVT or PAT, such as > 3-beat run in progress notes, telemetry strips; common with MI. Often over-looked, not documented. "SVT" without "paroxysmal" = code 42789 (non-CC)
Quadriplegia, Functional due to another condition phys. disability "Total care"	**78072**	3	The inability to move due to another condition (e.g., severe dementia, severe contractures, advanced arthritis, etc.). The patient is immobile because of a severe physical disability or frailty. The pt does not have the physical or mental ability to ambulate and functionally same as a paralyzed person. Look for "total care"; also maximum or severe disability on Braden score or nursing ADL assessment. (*CC* 2008 Q4). ICD-10: OCG defined as lack of ability to use one's limbs or to ambulate due to extreme debility, not associated with neurologic deficit or injury. The term must be specifically documented in the med record.
Respiratory Distress or Insufficiency: Acute (don't code c̄ COPD)	51882	2	Often occurs in cases of AMI, heart failure and pneumonia. Not coded if associated with COPD. "Acute" is required so query if only respiratory insufficiency or dyspnea is documented. May need to query for Acute Respiratory Failure if clinical criteria met.

Diagnosis	Codes	SI	Clinical Criteria/Indicators
Respiratory Failure: Acute/Unspecified or Acute on Chronic	**51881** **51884**	4	Defined as difficulty breathing with: (1) room air pO2 < 60 mmHg (SaO2 < 91%) or (2) P/F ratio <300 or (3) pCO2 >50 mmHg + pH < 7.35. Sequencing depends on circumstances of admission.
Respiratory Failure: Chronic any pt on chronic home O_2	51883	3	Often documented as "severe COPD on home 02" or "end-stage lung disease". Any patient on chronic home O2 has chronic respiratory failure. Chronically elevated pCO2 and bicarbonate (CO2 on electrolyte panel). "Acute on chronic" is an MCC.
Respiratory Failure: Following surgery	**51851, 51853**	4	If respiratory failure occurs following surgery, but is due another condition, such as COPD or heart failure – code 51881 or 51883 instead with the associated condition. Do not code if only normal, usual, expected ventilator management following surgery.
Schatzki's Ring	**7503**	3	A congenital esophageal stricture or stenosis which may remain undetected well into adulthood. Often contributes to symptoms of dysphagia or reflux and may require dilatation. Sometimes asymptomatic, incidental finding - then not coded. If specified as "acquired" = code 5303 (non-CC). Query if unspecified per *Coding Clinic* 2012 Q1P5.

Diagnosis	Codes	SI	Clinical Criteria/Indicators
Schizophrenia	29592	2	Most specified types or forms of schizophrenia, such as "paranoid" or "chronic" – unless stated as "in remission." Look for treatment with meds such as Risperdol, Zyprexa, Geodon, Abilify, Clozaril. Older drugs = Haldol, Mellaril, Thorazine. ICD-10: Must be specified to type, e.g., simple, paranoid, catatonic, disorganized, residual, other, to be CC.
Sepsis/SIRS -Usually primary -2° if p̄ admission or complication of care	**0380-03819, 0383-0388 0382,0389**	4 3	Sepsis = SIRS (9959x) due to infection. Sepsis usually sequenced as PDX when POA unless a complication of care. Will be a secondary diagnosis (MCC) when it occurs after admission or as a complication of care.
Shock	78550	4	Severe hypotension with blood pressure < 90/60 for > one hour from any cause.
Shock **Cardiogenic** **Septic** **Hypovolemic**	 **78551** **78552** **78559**	 4	Severe hypotension with blood pressure < 90/60 for > one hour due to cardiac failure, sepsis or hypovolemia (such as hemorrhagic shock).
SIRS, Noninfectious Always 2° dx	99593	2	SIRS associated with non-infectious conditions like severe burns, trauma, major surgery, pancreatitis, etc. without organ dysfunction. Codes 99593 is always a secondary diagnosis.

Diagnosis	Codes	SI	Clinical Criteria/Indicators
SIRS, Noninfectious with Organ Dysfunction KR Always 2° Dx	**99594**	4	SIRS associated with non-infectious conditions like severe burns, trauma, major surgery, pancreatitis, etc. with organ dysfunction. Codes 99594 is always secondary diagnosis.
Suicidal Ideation	V62.84	2	Typically associated with depression.
Thrombophlebitis / Phlebitis, Deep Veins of Upper or Lower Extremities	45111, 45119, 45181, 45183, 45189	3	Either acute or chronic. Deep veins only - unless a complication of care; upper or lower extremities. Fever, heat, redness, swelling, tenderness over vein or extremity. Look for device, implant, post-infusion.
Thrombophlebitis and Phlebitis, Following infusion Due to device, implant, graft	 9992 99662	 2 3	Either acute or chronic when a complication of care; upper or lower extremities. Fever, heat, redness, swelling, tenderness over vein or extremity. Look for device, implant, post-infusion.
Thrush, Oral	1120	2	Oral candidiasis: white patches in mouth; associated esophageal candidiasis common; recent antibiotics / immuno-suppressed; check for meds like Nystatin, Nizoral, Mycostatin, Diflucan.

Diagnosis	Codes	SI	Clinical Criteria/Indicators
TIA (Transient Ischemic Attack)	4359	2	Transient (< 24 hours) alteration in neurologic function, usually focal weakness, impaired speech, difficulty with balance or walking. Includes Basilar, Vertebral, Vertebro-basilar, and Subclavian Steal Syndromes. RX: Aspirin, Persantin, Aggrenox or Plavix®; carotid Doppler, echocardiogram (TEE).
Ulcer, Lower Limb	70710-70719	2	Any type except foot ulcer (70715). Look for an ulcer when wound infection or cellulitis present, PVD, diabetes. Distinguish from decubitus ulcer, which is most likely if foot ulcer is actually located on the heel or possibly ankle.
Urinary Tract Infection	5990	2	Urinalysis = bacteria, WBC, RBC, + leukocyte esterase, positive urine culture. Treatment with antibiotics, often no symptoms. Urosepsis defaults to "UTI". ICD-10: Urosepsis is not codable.
Ventricular fibrillation (DC alive)	**42741**	4	Always life-threatening, often terminal/fatal event. Common with AMI, severe CHF, electrolyte imbalance and certain drug toxicity or poisoning. Excluded as MCC when pt expires.
Ventricular Tachycardia	4271	3	3 or more consecutive wide-complex ventricular beats at a rate >120/min; common with AMI, severe CHF, electrolyte imbalance and certain drug toxicity or poisoning. Potentially life-threatening, especially if sustained.

Diagnosis	Codes	SI	Clinical Criteria/Indicators
Vertebral Compression Fracture – Non-traumatic (pathologic) – Traumatic code the same	 73313 8058	2	As a secondary diagnosis, the distinction between "traumatic" compression fractures (category 805) and pathologic ("non-traumatic") vertebral fractures (73313) does not affect DRG assignment; either qualifies as a CC. Should be acute or subacute condition requiring care / treatment / evaluation, not just an old or incidental finding on X-ray. ICD-10: Fractures with minimal trauma for pts with osteoporosis = pathologic. Traumatic vertebral fx must be specified to site (thoracic, lumbar, etc.)

BMI < 19 = V85.0
BMI ≥ 40 = V85.4x

Coders should not calculate the BMI. The BMI code assignment should be based on medical record documentation, which may be by a nonphysician such as a nutritionist or nurse. This is an exception to the guideline that requires code assignment be based on the documentation by the physician. The physician must provide some documentation of the clinical condition related to the BMI (such as weight loss, undernutrition, anorexia, weight gain, overweight, obesity, etc.). See Coding Clinic, Fourth Quarter 2005, Fourth Quarter 2008, Second Quarter 2010; and Official Coding Guidelines I.B.16.

ICD-10: BMI ≤ 19 (Z681) and BMI ≥ 40 (Z684x).

Conversion Table: See next page for BMI table.

1 kilogram = 2.2 lbs
CM x 2.54 = inch
Inch x 0.396 = CM
Meter = 39.6 inch

$$BMI = \frac{(WT\#) / 2.2}{[Ht'' / 39.6]^2} = Kg/m^2$$

Height	Body weight (in pounds)													
4'10"	91	96	100	105	110	115	119	124	129	134	138	143	167	191
4'11"	94	99	104	109	114	119	124	128	133	138	143	148	173	198
5'0"	97	102	107	112	118	123	128	133	138	143	148	153	179	204
5'1"	100	106	111	116	122	127	132	137	143	148	153	158	185	211
5'2"	104	109	115	120	126	131	136	142	147	153	158	164	191	218
5'3"	107	113	118	124	130	135	141	146	152	158	163	169	197	225
5'4"	110	116	122	128	134	140	145	151	157	163	169	174	204	232
5'5"	114	120	126	132	138	144	150	156	162	168	174	180	210	240
5'6"	118	124	130	136	142	148	155	161	167	173	179	186	216	247
5'7"	121	127	134	140	146	153	159	166	172	178	185	191	223	255
5'8"	125	131	138	144	151	158	164	171	177	184	190	197	230	262
5'9"	128	135	142	149	155	162	169	176	182	189	196	203	236	270
5'10"	132	139	146	153	160	167	174	181	188	195	202	209	243	278
5'11"	136	143	150	157	165	172	179	186	193	200	208	215	250	286
6'0"	140	147	154	162	169	177	184	191	199	206	213	221	258	294
6'1"	144	151	159	166	174	182	189	197	204	212	219	227	265	302
6'2"	148	155	163	171	179	186	194	202	210	218	225	233	272	311
6'3"	152	160	168	176	184	192	200	208	216	224	232	240	279	319
6'4"	156	164	172	180	189	197	205	213	221	230	238	246	287	328
BMI	**19**	**20**	**21**	**22**	**23**	**24**	**25**	**26**	**27**	**28**	**29**	**30**	**35**	**40**
	NORMAL						**OVERWEIGHT**					**OBESE**		

This section lists particular DRGs with the potential to reassign to another more optimal DRG.

For each DRG or DRG grouping the table includes:

1. Alternate or potential DRGs
2. Commonly associated CCs or MCCs
3. Alternate or more specific principal diagnoses
4. Other or more specific surgical or non-operating room procedures
5. Clinical indicators and tips for identifying these within the medical record

The list also includes DRGs that are targeted by audit contractors as indicated by the symbol.

If a DRG is *not* included in this section, this does not mean there are no opportunities to improve the DRG assignment. Always look for an *alternate principal diagnosis* based on the definition of the principal diagnosis or sequencing guidelines per coding rules discussed in the Guidelines section of this guide. Then, refer to the MCC/CC section for commonly missed MCC/CCs and clinical indicators to help identify them.

Abbreviations and symbols used in this section:

PDX = Principal Diagnosis, **SDX** = Secondary diagnosis

= Indicates high–risk Recovery Auditor target DRG

64-65-66 Cerebral Hemorrhage/Infarction RW 1.7417 / 1.0776 / 0.7566

Alt DRG	PDX / MCC-CC / Procedure		Tips
65	CC	Hemiparesis/hemiplegia (438.20)	Hemiparesis/hemiplegia that is residual from an old stroke or that was caused by a new acute CVA even if resolved at the time of hospital discharge can be coded as CC.
65	CC	tPA given in transferring hospital within 24 hrs	Add code V45.88 if patient received tPA at prior facility within last 24 hours.
64	MCC	Cerebral edema (348.5) Brain compression (348.4)	Clinically significant brain swelling/edema following CVA, cerebral hemorrhage (not just minor incidental finding) on CT or MRI; may cause brain/cerebral compression. Usually requires treatment with high-dose steroids.
85-87	PDX	CVA due to trauma	Look for evidence of trauma causing intracranial hemorrhage, e.g., fall. Subdural hematoma usually means trauma. Common in the elderly, alcoholics. RX: High-dose IV steroids. If unconscious > 1 hour = DRGs 82-84.
61-63	Non-OR PROC	tPA (99.10)	TPA is used to dissolve arterial blood clots. May document "aborted stroke" (coded as CVA) when thrombolytics are used. Pt presenting with symptoms of acute CVA who receive tPA have had a cerebral infarction. Not coded if tPA infusion is started in another facility prior to transfer – use code V45.88.

69 Transient Ischemic Attack — RW 0.6948

Alt DRG	PDX / MCC-CC / Procedure		Tips
64-66	PDX	Cerebral Infarction (KR)	Persistent neurologic deficit > 24 hours (despite negative imaging study), or positive imaging study (MRI/CT).
67-68	PDX	Cerebral or Precerebral Occlusion Thrombo-embolism without infarction	Any degree of narrowing, stenosis or occlusion of pre-cerebral artery (carotid, vertebral, basilar) in symptomatic area may be cause of TIA. Does not have to be "critical stenosis." Vertebral / basilar "syndromes" are classified as TIA; query regarding stenosis or occlusion as cause. Atrial fibrillation is common cause of cerebral embolism. Evaluation of TIA can sometimes be conducted in observation status within 24-48 hours (if ABCD2 score <4)

100-101 Seizures — RW 1.5185 / 0.7569

Alt DRG	PDX / MCC-CC / Procedure		Tips
54-55	PDX	Malignant Neoplasm, Brain	Underlying cause of seizure, e.g., brain tumor (primary or metastatic)
64-66	PDX	Cerebral Infarction	Underlying cause of seizure is CVA
67-68	PDX	Seizure – apoplectic, cerebral, brain (436)	Seizure described as apoplectic, cerebral, or brain

102-103 Headache — RW 1.0403 – 0.6663

Alt DRG	PDX / MCC-CC / Procedure		Tips
Multiple	PDX	Verify principal diagnosis	Identify alternative PDX and verify reason for admission. Typically, patients should not be admitted for migraines or other types of uncomplicated headaches and are more appropriately placed in observation.

149 Dysequilibrium — RW 0.6184

Alt DRG	PDX / MCC-CC / Procedure		Tips
64-66	PDX	CVA	Small stroke in cerebellum may not be seen on MRI/CT and can cause dysequilibrium lasting >24 hours = CVA.
67-68	PDX	Precerebral / cerebral occlusion or stenosis	As cause of disequilibrium/TIA (see below).
69	PDX	TIA	Cerebellar ischemia or unilateral weakness causing dysequilibrium < 24 hours duration.
312	PDX	Syncope	Review the record for evidence suggesting syncope, near-syncope, orthostatic or vaso-vagal hypotension

149 Dysequilibrium (cont.) RW 0.6184

Alt DRG	PDX / MCC-CC / Procedure		Tips
640-641	PDX	Electrolyte imbalance, dehydration	Dehydration, hypovolemia, other electrolyte imbalance are common causes of dizziness and vertigo. Verify lab values for evidence of dehydration (BUN, Na, K), poor skin turgor, IV fluids.
637-639	PDX	Diabetes	Diabetes or uncontrolled diabetes as reason for admission. Glucose > 400, ketosis; hyperosmolar; insulin or oral meds adjustment; endocrine consult.
811-812	PDX	Anemia	Anemia or blood loss anemia as cause of dizziness. Check for occult stool blood or if Hct < 30 / Hgb < 10, transfusion.

150-151 Epistaxis RW 1.3298 / 0.6557

Alt DRG	PDX / MCC-CC / Procedure		Tips
Multiple	PDX	Verify principal diagnosis	Verify reason for admission and PDX. Typically, patients are not admitted for uncomplicated epistaxis (nose bleed) and are more appropriately placed in observation. Look for hypertensive crisis/ "accelerated" hypertension, thrombocytopenia or coagulopathy (including over-anticoagulation with Coumadin or heparin or aspirin toxicity).

152-153 Otitis Media & URI

RW 1.0042 / 0.6439

Alt DRG	PDX / MCC-CC / Procedure		Tips
Multiple	PDX	Verify principal diagnosis	Alternative reason for admission or further specificity of principal diagnosis. Patients are not typically admitted for upper respiratory infection, acute sinusitis, laryngitis, otitis media, or uncomplicated influenza. If short stay, could be focus of RAC. Look for severe “mastoiditis” or malignant otitis media/externa (especially with diabetes). Pneumonia or complications of influenza.

177-179 Respiratory Infections

RW 1.9934 / 1.3955 / 0.9741

Alt DRG	PDX / MCC-CC / Procedure		Tips
871	PDX	Sepsis as PDX	Look for sepsis criteria. Sepsis usually sequenced first if POA. Pneumonia will be MCC when sepsis is PDX. See Key References – Sepsis.
207-208	PROC	Intubation, Ventilation	Patients may be intubated in ED before admission or emergently after admission with minimal documentation. Ventilator orders are often on a separate order form.
177	MCC	Acute Respiratory Failure KR	Blood gases (room air): $pO2 < 60$ = $SpO2$ (pulse ox) $< 91\%$, or $pCO2 > 50$ (usually with $pH < 7.35$).

180-182 Respiratory Neoplasms RW 1.7026 / 1.1725 / 0.7905

Alt DRG	PDX / MCC-CC / Procedure		Tips
166-168	PROC	Transbronchial Biopsy KR (33.27)	Transbronchial biopsy performed with bronchoscopy– review procedure note. Pathology report reveals lung/alveolar tissue biopsied. Do not confuse with endobronchial/bronchial biopsy (33.24) which does not change DRG.
177-179	PDX	“Complex” Pneumonia KR	Pneumonia (also “post-obstructive” pneumonia) as reason for admission. Gram-negative and staph are typically the cause.
181	CC	Malignant pleural effusion	Look for actual or potentially related symptoms, complication evaluation or treatment making it pertinent.

189 Respiratory Failure — RW 1.2184

Alt DRG	PDX / MCC-CC / Procedure		Tips
291	PDX	Acute Heart Failure as interrelated or co-equal PDX	Dyspnea, hypoxia, rales, wheezing, lower extremity edema, “volume overload”, left ventricular dysfunction; BNP >500; pulmonary edema/congestion, pleural effusion(s) or cardiac enlargement on chest x-ray. RX: IV Lasix, oxygen, nitrates including nitroglycerin.
207-208	PROC	Intubation, Ventilation	Patients may be intubated in ED before admission or emergently after admission with minimal documentation. Ventilator orders are often on a separate order form.
003-004	PROC	Tracheostomy	Temporary or permanent tracheostomy (31.1, 31.29) during admission

190-192 COPD — RW 1.1708 / 0.9343 / 0.7120

Alt DRG	PDX / MCC-CC / Procedure		Tips
189 190	PDX MCC	Acute respiratory failure KR (518.81)	Blood gases (room air): pO2 < 60 = SpO2 (pulse ox) < 91 %, or pCO2 > 50 (usually with pH < 7.35). Look for BiPAP, high-flow oxygen. Sequencing depends on circumstances and focus of admission.

190-192 COPD (cont.)

Alt DRG	PDX / MCC-CC / Procedure		Tips
191	CC	Chronic Respiratory Failure (51883)	"Severe COPD on home 02". "end-stage lung disease"; chronically elevated pCO2 and HCO3 (CO2 on electrolyte panel); chronic hypoxia.
190	MCC	Simple Pneumonia	If pneumonia co-equal with COPD and no other MCC, sequence COPD as PDX and pneumonia as SDX; if another MCC, sequence pneumonia as PDX. Treatment of simple pneumonia and AECOPD likely to be the same: antibiotics, O2 therapy, IV steroids, other respiratory care modalities.
180-182	PDX	Respiratory Neoplasm as interrelated principal diagnosis	Shortness of breath and other respiratory problems could be due to either COPD or progression of respiratory malignancy (if POA). If diagnosed or treated on current admission, sequence neoplasm as PDX if meets definition of PDX.
175-176	PDX	Pulmonary embolism/ thrombus	May be underlying cause of COPD exacerbation or shortness of breath. Elevated D-dimer; positive chest CT with contrast.
166-168	PROC	Transbronchial Biopsy (33.27)	Transbronchial biopsy performed with bronchoscopy– review procedure note. Pathology report reveals lung/alveolar tissue biopsied. Do not confuse with endobronchial/bronchial biopsy (33.24) which does not change DRG.
207-208	PROC	Intubation, Ventilation	Patients may be intubated in ED before admission or emergently after admission with minimal documentation. Ventilator orders are often on a separate order form.

193-195 Simple Pneumonia

RW 1.4550 / 0.9771 / 0.6997

Alt DRG	PDX / MCC-CC / Procedure		Tips
177-179	PDX	Aspiration pneumonia	Nursing home patient, recent vomiting, debilitated, dysphagia, GERD, history of CVA, alcoholism, NG tube. Often lower lobe infiltrate (right more common) RX Flagyl, Clindamycin, Zosyn.
177-179	PDX	Possible Staph / MRSA pneumonia Gram-negative	Documentation of "HCAP" (healthcare associated pneumonia) which is most often caused by staph and/or gram-negatives. *See Key References – Pneumonia for further detail on HCAP.*
193	MCC	Acute Respiratory Failure	Blood gases (room air): pO2 < 60 = SpO2 (pulse ox) < 91 %, or pCO2 > 50 (usually with pH < 7.35). BiPAP, high-flow oxygen, other respiratory care modalities.
871	PDX	Sepsis	Look for sepsis criteria. Sepsis usually sequenced first if POA. Pneumonia will be MCC when sepsis is PDX.
190	PDX	Acute Exacerbation of COPD	If pneumonia co-equal with COPD and no other MCC, sequence AECOPD as PDX and pneumonia as SDX; if another MCC, sequence pneumonia as PDX. AECOPD is recognized by worsening O2 sat and/or symptoms, fever, increased O2 requirements need for inpatient care. Treatment of pneumonia and AECOPD likely to be the same: Antibiotics, O2 therapy, IV steroids, other respiratory care modalities.

193-195 Simple Pneumonia (continued)

Alt DRG	PDX / MCC-CC / Procedure		Tips
190	PDX	Acute Exacerbation of COPD	If pneumonia co-equal with COPD and no other MCC, sequence AECOPD as PDX and pneumonia as SDX; if another MCC, sequence pneumonia as PDX. AECOPD is recognized by worsening O2 sat and/or symptoms, fever, increased O2 requirements need for inpatient care. Treatment of pneumonia and AECOPD likely to be the same: Antibiotics, O2 therapy, IV steroids, other respiratory care modalities.

202-203 Bronchitis & Asthma

RW 0.8678 / 0.6391

Alt DRG	PDX / MCC-CC / Procedure		Tips
190-192	PDX	Acute bronchitis with COPD (49122, 49322)	Acute bronchitis with COPD, or asthma with COPD. History of COPD, COPD on CXR, history of chronic or recurrent bronchitis.
177-179	PDX	Aspiration bronchitis (507.0)	Same risk factors as aspiration pneumonia (NH patient, recent vomiting, debilitated, dysphagia, GERD, history of CVA, alcoholism, NG tube), but patient develops bronchitis with negative chest x-ray, rather than pneumonia.
193-195	PDX	Simple Pneumonia (486)	Evidence of pneumonia: fever, chest pain, difficulty breathing, sputum production, shortness of breath, positive chest x-ray.

204 Respiratory Signs & Symptoms — RW 0.6780

Alt DRG	PDX / MCC-CC / Procedure		Tips
Multiple	PDX	Verify Principal Diagnosis	More specific condition that is causing the symptoms or an alternate PDX. Selection of a symptom code is primarily the reason for assignment to this DRG, such as dyspnea, respiratory distress, hemoptysis, etc. Symptom is not PDX when explained by a definitive diagnosis. *See Coding Guidelines – Signs and Symptoms.*

205-206 Other Respiratory System Diagnoses — RW 1.3935 / 0.7911

Alt DRG	PDX / MCC-CC / Procedure		Tips
Multiple	PDX	Alternative principal diagnosis	Verify that the most specific diagnosis is used as principal diagnosis considering all alternatives.

207-208 Respiratory System Diagnosis with Ventilator — RW 5.2556 / 2.2871

Alt DRG	PDX / MCC-CC / Procedure		Tips
Multiple	PDX	Respiratory diagnosis is PDX	Verify physician documentation adequately supports a respiratory diagnosis as PDX to ensure appropriate assignment to this DRG.

207-208 Respiratory System Diagnosis with Ventilator — RW 5.2556 / 2.2871

Alt DRG	PDX / MCC-CC / Procedure		Tips
207	PROC	Duration of ventilation > 96 hours KR	Carefully calculate duration of ventilation. RAC focuses on PDX assignment and > 96 hours ventilator support.

247 Percutaneous CV Proc w Drug Eluting Stent — RW 2.0408
249 Percutaneous CV Proc w Non-Drug Eluting Stent — RW 1.8245

Alt DRG	PDX / MCC-CC / Procedure		Tips
OBS	PDX	Verify reason for admission	Patients should be admitted emergently with an acute condition, i.e., unstable angina, acute coronary syndrome, acute MI, heart failure, etc. which should be coded. High risk for medical necessity denial if coronary stent not done urgently. Also verify inpatient order is present.
246-248	MCC	Postop complication	Acute MI or other complications following PCI/stent insertion as MCCs occurring during admission, or PDX (sometimes assigned to other DRGs) if admitted following outpatient surgery.
246-248	PROC	Number of stents or vessels (4 or more)	Review the content of the operative report carefully to determine the number of stents inserted and vessels involved: 4 or more stents or vessels is equivalent to an MCC and changes the DRG.

252-254 Other Vascular Procedures RW 3.1477 / 2.5172 / 1.7012

Alt DRG	PDX / MCC-CC / Procedure		Tips
Multiple DRGs	PDX	Verify Reason for Admission	Reason for admission like post-op complication or additional procedures. Do not overlook an obscure invasive radiology note for inpatient. When not urgent condition, these procedures are usually performed on outpatient basis. RAC focus on most procedures included in this DRG if performed as inpatient. Also verify inpatient order.
Multiple DRGs	PDX	Post-op Complication	Look for post-op complication as reason for admission from ambulatory surgery.
252-253	CC or MCC	Acute Renal Failure OR Acute Tubular Necrosis (ATN) KR	Acute Renal Failure following IV contrast occurs commonly and always due to ATN (if physician knows and will document). Look for non-specific documentation of "renal insufficiency" or indicators: increase Creatinine by change to: ≥ 0.3 within 48 hours or to ≥ 1.5 x baseline. ATN usually takes > 72 hours for renal function toward return to baseline.
673-674	PDX	ATN or acute renal failure complicating procedure	Post-op ATN or acute renal failure as reason for inpatient admission from ambulatory surgery. See above.

282 Acute Myocardial Infarction without CC/MCC — RW 0.7551

Alt DRG	PDX / MCC-CC / Procedure		Tips
281	CC	Cardiac arrhythmia following MI	V-Tach (427.1), PSVT (427.0), PAT (427.0), Atrial flutter (427.32). Often in telemetry strips, nursing notes, progress notes. Indications such as "3-beat run V-tach" are usually significant and "monitored"
281	CC	Pericarditis following MI	Dressler's Syndrome: Pericarditis following acute MI; pleuritic chest pain, pericardial "friction rub", fever and/or elevated sed rate (ESR).
280	MCC	Acute Heart Failure, Systolic/Diastolic	Often associated with acute MI. Dyspnea, hypoxia, rales, wheezing, "volume overload", left ventricular dysfunction; BNP >500; pulmonary edema/congestion, pleural effusion(s) or cardiac enlargement on chest x-ray. RX: IV Lasix, oxygen, nitrates including nitroglycerin.

292-293 Heart Failure with CC or without CC/MCC — RW 0.9938 / 0.6723

Alt DRG	PDX / MCC-CC / Procedure		Tips
189 / 291	PDX MCC	Acute Respiratory Failure	Blood gases (room air): $pO_2 < 60 = SpO_2$ (pulse ox) < 91%, or $pCO_2 > 50$ (usually with pH < 7.35); RX: BiPAP, high-flow oxygen, other respiratory care modalities. Sequencing depends on circumstances and focus of admission.

292-293 Heart Failure with CC or without CC/MCC (cont.) RW 0.9938 / 0.6723

Alt DRG	PDX / MCC-CC / Procedure		Tips
291	PDX	Hypertensive Heart Disease (HHD) with CKD (404.91)	Look for hypertension as possible cause of heart failure (hypertensive heart disease) with co-existing CKD. The provider must specifically link the causal relationship between the hypertension and heart failure. A diagnosis of “hypertensive cardiomyopathy” establishes this link when heart failure is also documented in the record. HHD with CKD + heart failure (if specified as acute systolic or diastolic) is assigned to DRG 291. Code 404.91 is sequenced first, with acute systolic or diastolic heart failure as MCC.
280-282	PDX	Acute MI (410.x1)	Patient admitted with acute MI (410.x1) in addition to or associated with heart failure. Elevated Troponin documentation of ACS, unstable angina, hypotension suggests possible MI

296-298 Cardiac Arrest, Unexplained — RW 1.3013 / 0.6063 / 0.4260

Alt DRG	PDX / MCC-CC / Procedure		Tips
207-208 280 Other	PDX	Other co-equal or interrelated diagnosis, or cause of the cardiac arrest	Cardiac arrest (427.5) should rarely be used as the PDX when a patient is admitted to the hospital, but rather its consequences. Cardiac arrest is abrupt cessation of cardiac contraction usually due to ventricular fibrillation or asystole. Most common causes include: respiratory failure, acute MI, ventricular fib/tach, severe heart block, hyperkalemia, massive hemorrhage, pulmonary embolus, trauma. If mechanical ventilation required, respiratory failure as the primary focus of admission would usually be the principal diagnosis, not cardiac arrest. Look also for evaluation and treatment of other potentially life threatening conditions. Once a patient is resuscitated, cardiac arrest is rarely the focus of admission but rather its sequelae or complications.

311 Angina — RW 0.5649

Alt DRG	PDX / MCC-CC / Procedure		Tips
302-303 280-282	PDX	Coronary Artery Disease (CAD) Acute MI	Angina is a symptom of underlying CAD. Angina may occur w/o CAD (e.g., Prinzmetal's angina = coronary artery spasm). If CAD mentioned with angina, code CAD first. "ACS" is coded as Unstable Angina, but if Troponin elevated may be an MI (NSTEMI).

312 Syncope RW 0.7228

Alt DRG	PDX / MCC-CC / Procedure		Tips
308-310	PDX	Cardiac arrhythmia as cause of syncope	Syncope is a symptom and defined as transient loss of consciousness without subsequent sequelae. Most common cause (if not due to orthostatic hypotension) is cardiac arrhythmia, which may be difficult to diagnose without prolonged cardiac event monitoring, particularly when no cause is identified by the initial work-up. In this case, a query is usually warranted for possible or suspected arrhythmia as the likely cause.
308-310	PDX	Heart block, 2nd (Mobitz II) or 3rd degree	Note that 1st degree heart block and 2nd degree heart block (Mobitz 1) usually have no symptoms and do not cause syncope, although they may be indicators of higher degree heart block especially if any type of bundle branch block is also present.
811-812	PDX	Anemia	Acute blood-loss anemia frequently causes syncope. Chronic anemia usually develops gradually and is well tolerated until it becomes severe (H/H < 8/24). Evaluation of chronic GI blood loss in stable patients may be conducted on an outpatient basis. Evaluation of GI blood loss in stable patients should be conducted on an outpatient basis.

312 Syncope (continued)

Alt DRG	PDX / MCC-CC / Procedure		Tips
640-641	PDX	Dehydration / Hypovolemia	Electrolyte imbalance, elevated BUN. If elevated creatinine, may be acute renal failure. Patients with simple dehydration are likely candidates for observation status.
637-639	PDX	Hypoglycemia	Low blood sugar – usually does not cause unconsciousness/ syncope unless <40 almost always due to insulin or oral diabetic medication (adverse effect of poisoning). RX: Oral or parenteral glucose administration, Glucagon, modification of diabetic medications. Pts with uncomplicated hypoglycemia are likely candidates for observation status. If due to oral meds inpatient likely needed.
67-68	PDX	Cerebral / precerebral occlusion or stenosis	Stenosis of vertebrobasilar (VB) or bilateral carotid arteries; usually not other pre-cerebral/cerebral arteries. Thrombosis/ embolism not a likely cause of syncope. VB "syndrome/insufficiency" is classified as TIA, so an opportunity to query for underlying cause = stenosis.
73-74	PDX	DM autonomic neuropathy	Autonomic neuropathy, dysfunction, insufficiency in diabetic patient specified as cause of syncope or orthostatic hypotension

313 Chest Pain RW 0.5992

Alt DRG	PDX / MCC-CC / Procedure		Tips
204	PDX	"Chest wall" or "pleuritic" pain (786.52)	Pleuritic "painful respiration"; "anterior" chest wall pain. Compare with non-specific terms precordial, substernal, mid-sternal = unspecified chest pain. RX: NSAIDS, acetaminophen, muscle relaxers.
205-206	PDX	Hyperventilation syndrome (306.1)	Similar to "anxiety" but more severe; extreme SOB, rapid breathing, "panicked"; numbness in extremities, face. RX: Anxiolytics, sedatives. Provider must connect to chest pain (e.g., "chest pain probably due to hyperventilation") since not routinely associated with anxiety.
205-206	PDX	Costo-chrondritis / Tietze disease (733.6)	Localized point tenderness over one or more costo-chrondral junctions; worsened by movement/ position. RX: NSAIDS, acetaminophen. Connection by provider not required since chest pain is always an associated symptom.
880	PDX	Anxiety (300.00) as cause of chest pain	Pain usually vague, poorly localized; SOB common. May have precipitating event (recent family illness, domestic difficulties). RX: Anxiolytic, sedatives. Physician must connect chest pain to anxiety (e.g., "chest pain probably due to anxiety") since chest pain is not routinely associated with anxiety.

313 Chest Pain (continued)

Alt DRG	PDX / MCC-CC / Procedure		Tips
391-392	PDX	GERD, Reflux, Esophagitis or Esophageal Spasm	Pain may be burning, "indigestion", pressure, tightness, squeezing: +/- relief with antacid, sometimes worse when lying down; regurgitation with food or liquids. In cases of dyspepsia, gastritis, or peptic ulcer, sometimes nausea / vomiting sometimes occur. Connection with chest pain may or may not be required depending on circumstances. RX: Prilosec, Axid, H-2 blockers, antacids, Reglan; GI studies performed or planned.
811-812	PDX	Anemia (285.9)	Acute anemia, including chronic if severe enough (usually Hct < 30, Hgb < 8), may be the underlying cause of the chest pain if connected/specified by provider.
444-446	PDX	Gallstones (cholelithiasis) Biliary Colic (with or without gallstones) Cholecystitis (especially "chronic")	Location: RUQ, substernal, epigastric, back, right shoulder; may have nausea, vomiting; pain is routinely associated with biliary colic and cholecystitis Gallstones are often asymptomatic and not routinely associated with pain; therefore, the physician must connect to the chest pain. US of gallbladder: stones, "sludge", inflamed, thickened gallbladder; HIDA scan may show non-function of gall bladder. RX: Narcotic analgesics; antibiotics

341-343 Appendectomy without Complex PDX RW 2.1821 / 1.2968 / 0.9358

Alt DRG	PDX / MCC-CC / Procedure		Tips
338-340	Complex DX	Appendicitis complicated by generalized peritonitis (5400), or Appendiceal abscess (5401)	Look for "peritonitis" or "abscess" in pre- or post-op documentation including CT reports and in op-note. Reference to "exudate", "purulence", "serositis" or similar terms, especially when small bowel involved. Any mention of "peritonitis", code 5400. If both peritonitis and abscess are mentioned, assign 5401 only.
853-854	PDX	Sepsis due to appendicitis	Look for clinical criteria for Sepsis (SIRS due to infection). Surgeons do not customarily consider healthy, "non-toxic" patients with simple, uncomplicated appendicitis to have sepsis even when fever, tachycardia, and leukocytosis may be present, since these are clinically so intrinsic to the diagnosis. The same may not be true for elderly or chronically ill individuals or with perforation/abcess where sepsis may occur.
335-337	PROC	Lysis of adhesions, peritoneal (54.5x)	To be coded 54.5x, the adhesions must be significant (extensive or dense, causing an obstruction; requiring resection, enterotomy, substantial "take-down"; or otherwise altering the procedure). Do not code based solely on mention of adhesions or simple lysis in the operative report. *See Coding Clinic 1990, Q4 and 1994, Q3*

350-352 Inguinal & Femoral Hernia Procedure RW 2.4598 / 1.3761 / 0.9239

Alt DRG	PDX / MCC-CC / Procedure		Tips
987-989	PDX	Complication following surgery	Reason for admission (Principal Diagnosis) is a complication or other condition following ambulatory surgery, such as cardiac arrhythmia, etc. In these cases, the surgical diagnosis would be listed as a SDX and the surgical procedure also coded.
353-355	PROC	Verify type of hernia repaired.	If not inguinal or femoral hernia repair, PDX code and procedure code will change.
335-337	PROC	Lysis of adhesions, peritoneal (54.5x) takes priority as Principal	To be coded 54.5x, the adhesions must be significant (extensive or dense, causing an obstruction; requiring resection, enterotomy, substantial "take-down"; or otherwise altering the procedure). Do not code based solely on mention of adhesions or simple lysis in the operative report. *See Coding Clinics, 1990, Q4 and 1994, Q3*

353-355 Hernia Procedures Exc Inguinal & Femoral   RW 2.7885 / 1.6401 / 1.1783

Alt DRG	PDX / MCC-CC / Procedure		Tips
907-909	PDX	Failed mesh graft (996.59) as PDX	Look for repeat incisional or ventral hernia repair for failed mesh graft
335-337	PROC	Lysis of adhesions, peritoneal (54.5x) takes priority as Principal	To be coded 54.5x, the adhesions must be significant (extensive or dense, causing an obstruction; requiring resection, enterotomy, substantial "take-down"; or otherwise altering the procedure). Do not code based solely on mention of adhesions or simple lysis in the operative report. *See Coding Clinics, 1990, Q4 and 1994, Q3*
329-331	PROC	Manipulation of intestine (46.82)	Hernia repairs usually include reduction of the bowel. A torsed, twisted or kinked bowel may require a manipulation or manual correction.

377-379 GI Hemorrhage RW 1.7629 / 1.0029 / 0.6937

Alt DRG	PDX / MCC-CC / Procedure		Tips
378	CC	Acute blood loss anemia	Anemia (or more anemic) due to blood loss; often associated with GI bleeding. Transfusion not required if "monitored". Be aware if "chronic" GI bleeding not evaluated and the only treatment is transfusion, anemia would be the likely PDX. *See also Key References – Anemia*
385-387	PDX	Inflammatory bowel disease as cause of GI bleeding: ulcerative colitis or Crohn's disease (regional enteritis)	Colicky pain, bowel obstruction (partial or complete); diarrhea, often bloody; GI bleeding due to erosions/ulceration/fistula. Check colonoscopy and biopsy reports for this diagnosis. "Hemorrhagic" ulcerative colitis or Crohn's is a descriptive term and does not by itself indicate GI bleeding or hemorrhage which must be separately identified. RX: antibiotics, steroids, sulfa-derivatives, anti-metabolites, TNF inhibitors.
368-370	PDX	Esophageal Varices	Esophageal varices are almost always due to cirrhosis of liver (alcoholic or non-alcoholic) with associated portal hypertension. Variceal bleeding is often massive with vomiting bright red blood. Look for associated acute blood loss/post-hemorrhagic anemia. If cirrhosis of liver documented, code cirrhosis first (see DRG 432 below)

377-379 GI Hemorrhage (continued)

Alt DRG	PDX / MCC-CC / Procedure		Tips
432	PDX	Esophageal Varices with Liver Cirrhosis	If source of hemorrhage is esophageal varices (456.20) and the patient has cirrhosis of liver (alcoholic or non-alcoholic), cirrhosis of liver would be sequenced as principal diagnosis. *See ICD-9-CM Tabular Index instructions.*
441	PDX	Esophageal Varices with Portal Hypertension	If source of hemorrhage is esophageal varices (456.20) and the patient has portal hypertension, without cirrhosis, portal hypertension (572.3) would be sequenced as principal diagnosis.
374-376	PDX	Evidence malignancy as cause of GI bleed	Underlying malignancy must be treated, evaluated or undergoing workup to be sequenced as PDX. *See also Coding Guidelines – Neoplasms.*

383-384 Uncomplicated Peptic Ulcer RW 1.3850 / 0.8501

Alt DRG	PDX / MCC-CC / Procedure		Tips
380-382	PDX	Esophageal ulcer (530.2x), Barrett's esophagus (530.85), Obstructed ulcer	Look for esophageal ulcer or Barrett's esophagus (lining of the esophagus is damaged by stomach acid) on UGI or endoscopy, or diagnosis of ulcer with obstruction.

385-387 Inflammatory Bowel Disease — RW 1.7973 / 1.0097 / 0.7533

Alt DRG	PDX / MCC-CC / Procedure		Tips
371-373	PDX	Enteritis/Colitis: Clostridium difficile (008.45) Campylobacter (008.43) E. coli (008.00) Bacterial (008.5)	Infection of the bowel causing severe diarrhea (often bloody), dehydration and/or electrolyte imbalance. May be fatal especially extremes of age. C. diff is common with recent antibiotic therapy, especially broad-spectrum; highly-contagious; nursing home status or recent hospitalization. Stool test for C. diff is not a culture, identifies the toxin, not the organism; physicians often consider C. diff infection suspected, likely, possible even when stool test is negative (look for on-going treatment). RX: C. Diff usually treated with Flagyl, sometimes oral Vancomycin; others typically bactrim, tetracycline, erythromycin E. coli (common form of travelers' diarrhea) and Campylobacter similar to C. diff. Bacterial similar to above but less specific. Sepsis not unusual with these infections.
386	CC	GI bleeding	GI bleeding may be associated with ulceration, erosions, fistula. Look for bloody diarrhea, positive stool blood, rectal bleeding, drop in Hgb/Hct in a patient with ulcerative/regional colitis. "Hemorrhagic" is a descriptive term and does not by itself indicate GI bleeding or hemorrhage which should be separately identified.

391-392 Esophagitis, Gastroent, & Digestive Disorders RW 1.1903 / 0.7395

Alt DRG	PDX / MCC-CC / Procedure		Tips
73-74	PDX	Diabetic Gastroparesis	Very common manifestation of diabetes: usually vomiting without diarrhea; dilated stomach / abdominal pressure; frequently spontaneous without precipitating event, tends to be recurrent. Caused by autonomic neuropathy. Often overlooked or confused with gastritis, peptic disease, other GI disorders. RX: Reglan (metoclopramide) is the best treatment, and very specific for gastroparesis. Phenergan, other anti-emetics less effective.
393-395	PDX	Radiation or Toxic Gastroenteritis / Colitis (558.1, 558.2)	Diarrhea, pain, bleeding, obstruction secondary to radiation therapy or toxin. If due to chemotherapy (558.9), DRG remains 391-392.
388-390	PDX	Bowel Obstruction, Ileus	Evidence of ileus, bowel obstruction on imaging; constipation, obstipation. RX: NPO, IVF, NG tube.
393-395	PDX	Ischemic enteritis/ colitis (557.x)	Ischemic colitis (557.x) = ischemic changes of mucosa of colon or small bowel due to loss of blood supply.
380-382	PDX	Esophageal Ulcer or Obstructed Ulcer	Endoscopy or UGI indicates esophageal ulcer or diagnosis of ulcer with obstruction

391-392 Esophagitis, Gastroent, & Digestive Disorders (continued)

Alt DRG	PDX / MCC-CC / Procedure		Tips
371-373	PDX	Enteritis/Colitis: Clostridium difficile (008.45) Campylobacter (008.43) E. coli (008.00) Bacterial (008.5)	Infection of the bowel causing severe diarrhea (often bloody), dehydration and/or electrolyte imbalance. May be fatal especially extremes of age. C. diff is common with recent antibiotic therapy, especially broad-spectrum; highly-contagious; NH status or recent hospitalization. Stool test for C. diff is not a culture, identifies the toxin, not the organism; physicians often consider C. diff infection possible even when stool test is negative (look for on-going treatment). RX: C.diff usually treated with Flagyl, sometimes oral Vancomycin;others typically bactrim, tetracycline, erythromycin E. coli (common form of travelers' diarrhea) and Campylobacter similar to C. diff. Bacterial similar to above but less specific. Sepsis not unusual with these infections.
374-375	PDX	Villous adenoma (235.5)	Villous adenomas may secrete large amounts of mucous causing abdominal pain and diarrhea.
383-384	PDX	Gastric, Peptic, Duodenal Ulcer	Look for gastric, peptic, duodenal ulcer as cause of gastroenteritis, abdominal pain and/or vomiting. Endoscopy or x-ray may indicate ulcer or stress ulcer. RX: Tagamet, Pepcid, Carafate.

391-392 Esophagitis, Gastroent, & Digestive Disorders (continued)

Alt DRG	PDX / MCC-CC / Procedure		Tips
377-379	PDX	GI Bleeding, Melena	Drop in H/H, anemia, or blood in stool may indicate evidence of GI bleeding as primary reason for admission.
385-387	PDX	Inflammatory bowel or Crohn's Disease, Ulcerative Colitis	Regional enteritis. Colicky pain, bowel obstruction (partial or complete); diarrhea, often bloody. RX: antibiotics, steroids, sulfa-derivatives, anti-metabolites, TNF inhibitors.

393-394 Other Digestive System Diagnoses RW 1.6563 / 0.9653

Alt DRG	PDX / MCC-CC / Procedure		Tips
Multiple Medical DRGs	PDX	Verify principal diagnosis	Be sure the PDX accurately reflects the reason for admission and acuity. Inpatient admission is not usually required for many of the conditions that are assigned to this DRG, such as colon polyps, hernia, hemorrhoids, anal abscess, unless there is GI bleeding or surgery performed. These conditions as PDX are a RAC focus.

417-419 Lap Cholecystectomy — RW 2.4784 / 1.6536 / 1.2239

Alt DRG	PDX / MCC-CC / Procedure		Tips
987-988	PDX	Complication following surgery	Reason for admission (principal diagnosis) is a complication or other condition *following ambulatory surgery*, such as cardiac arrhythmia, etc. In these cases, the surgical diagnosis would be listed as a SDX and the surgical procedure also coded.
414-416	PROC	Open chole-cystectomy (51.22)	Lap cholecystectomy converted to an open cholecystectomy.
412-413	PROC	Common bile duct exploration	Look for common bile duct exploration performed: Procedure codes 51.41, 51.42, or 51.51.

432 Cirrhosis & Alcoholic Hepatitis w MCC — RW 1.7150

Alt DRG	PDX / MCC-CC / Procedure		Tips
441-443	PDX	Hepatic Encephalopathy as reason for admission	In the absence of bleeding varices, patients are not typically admitted for liver cirrhosis itself since this is a chronic condition . Hepatic encephalopathy or coma is a potentially life-threatening condition. If it is the primary reason for admission, it would be sequenced as PDX. *See Coding Clinic 2002, Q1, P3.*

468 Revision of Hip or Knee Replacement without CC/MCC — RW 2.7624

Alt DRG	PDX / MCC-CC / Procedure		Tips
467	CC	Acute blood loss anemia KR	Significant blood loss anemia following major orthopedic surgery is common. Check for drop in Hgb/Hct below normal or pre-op baseline. Transfusion not required, if monitored. If transfusion given, acute blood loss anemia should almost always be diagnosed.

469-470 Major Joint Replacement or Reattach of Lower Extremity — RW 3.4377 / 2.1463

Alt DRG	PDX / MCC-CC / Procedure		Tips
461-462	PROC	Bilateral joint replacement	Bilateral joint replacements must be coded twice.

480-482 Hip & Femur Procedure Except Major Joint — RW 3.0694 / 1.9721 / 1.6305

Alt DRG	PDX / MCC-CC / Procedure		Tips
481	CC	Acute blood loss KR anemia as CC	Blood loss anemia due to the fracture and/or surgery is common. Check for drop in Hgb/Hct below normal or pre-op baseline. Transfusion not required, if monitored. If transfusion given, acute blood loss anemia should almost always be diagnosed.
956	PDX	Additional traumatic condition	If procedure performed for a diagnosis that is due to trauma, look for evidence of other significant trauma in a separate organ system, e.g., closed skull fracture with brief loss of consciousness (803.02).
477-479	PROC	Diagnostic bone biopsy (77.4x)	Diagnostic bone biopsy performed during the hip procedure. Check op-note carefully. Look for pathology report.

535-536 Fractures of Hip & Pelvis   RW 1.3085 / 0.7091

Alt DRG	PDX / MCC-CC / Procedure		Tips
480-482 469-470	PROC	ORIF, Hip replacement	Look for operative procedure.
542-544	PDX	Pathologic fracture	If no surgical procedure, look for evidence of pathologic/osteoporotic fracture: Minimal or no trauma (fall < 6 ft) and abnormal bone. Hip or pelvic fractures specified as due to osteoporosis (or “osteoporotic”), neoplasm (or “malignant“), other bone diseases, or if documented as insufficiency, spontaneous, or chronic fracture (733.13). Also, “stress” fracture (733.95).

551-552 Medical Back Problem RW 1.6317 / 0.8467

Alt DRG	PDX / MCC-CC / Procedure		Tips
542-544	PDX	Pathologic vertebral fracture	Minimal or no trauma (fall < 6 ft) and abnormal bone Vertebral fracture specified as due to osteoporosis (or "osteoporotic"), neoplasm (or "malignant"), other bone diseases, or if documented as insufficiency, non-traumatic, spontaneous, or chronic fracture (733.13).); Also, vertebral "stress" fracture (733.95) or "collapsed vertebra" (733.13) Back pain alone is usually not sufficient to meet inpatient level of care criteria, but may be treated in observation status for 24-48 hrs to control pain.
388-390	PDX	Bowel obstruction	Look for other possible causes of back pain, such as bowel obstruction. Other possible causes: pancreatitis, or shingles (H. zoster), gallbladder, kidney problems.
97-99	PDX	Back pain due to arachnoiditis (322.9)	Characterized by severe stinging, burning pain, and neurologic problems. Pain disorder caused by the inflammation of the arachnoid, one of the membranes that surround and protect the spinal cord nerves. Review CT/MRI for thickened or clumped nerve roots.

570-572 Skin Debridement RW 2.4154 / 1.4906 / 1.0077

Alt DRG	PDX / MCC-CC / Procedure		Tips
40-42 264	PDX	Diabetic neuropathy (250.6x) Diabetic PVD or circulatory disease (250.7x)	If patient has diabetes: Ulcer may be due to diabetic neuropathy (250.6x), or due to diabetic circulatory system (peripheral vascular) disease (250.7x) as cause of ulcer or cellulitis, which would be sequenced as PDX. Verify procedure is "excisional". RAC focus on excisional debridement documentation. *See Key References –Debridement.*
571	CC	Cellulitis	Look for evidence of cellulitis associated with skin ulcer when no MCC/CC; unlikely to be PDX if excisional debridement performed for ulcer.

592-594 Skin Ulcers RW 1.4131 / 1.0094 / 0.6814

Alt DRG	PDX / MCC-CC / Procedure		Tips
603-604	PDX	Cellulitis	Look for evidence of cellulitis associated with skin ulcer; sequencing depends upon focus of admission or may be co-equal.
593	CC	Cellulitis	Look for evidence of cellulitis associated with skin ulcer when no MCC/CC; sequencing depends upon focus of admission.

592-594 Skin Ulcers (cont.)

Alt DRG	PDX / MCC-CC / Procedure		Tips
570-572	PROC	Excisional Debridement (86.22) KR	Surgical removal or "cutting away" of devitalized tissue; use of term "Excisional" is crucial. Can be performed in OR, ER, "minor procedure room" or bedside. Verify procedure is appropriately documented as "excisional". RAC focus on excisional debridement documentation.

602-603 Cellulitis — RW 1.4607 / 0.8402

Alt DRG	PDX / MCC-CC / Procedure		Tips
871-872	PDX	Sepsis	Look for clinical criteria for Sepsis (SIRS due to Infection) – *See Key References for Sepsis.* Cellulitis can usually be treated initially on an outpatient basis unless sepsis is present. Immune suppression or failed outpatient treatment with oral antibiotics are also reasons for inpatient admission.

602-603 Cellulitis (cont.)

Alt DRG	PDX / MCC-CC / Procedure		Tips
593	PDX	Skin Ulcer	If patient admitted with both cellulitis and skin ulcer that are co-equal and there is no MCC, sequence skin ulcer as PDX. Cellulitis will be CC.
570-572	PROC	Excisional debridement (86.22) KR	If abscess or skin ulcer present, look for evidence of "excisional" debridement. Surgical removal or "cutting away" of devitalized tissue; use of term "Excisional" is crucial. Can be performed in OR, ER, "minor procedure room" or bedside. Verify procedure is appropriately documented as "excisional". RAC focus on excisional debridement documentation.

637-639 Diabetes — RW 1.3888 / 0.8252 / 0.5708

Alt DRG	PDX / MCC-CC / Procedure		Tips
73-74	PDX	DM-Associated Neuropathy	Look for associated diabetic complications such as gastroparesis, peripheral neuropathy, as PDX, code 250.6x.
299-301	PDX	DM-Associated Peripheral Vascular or Circulatory	Look for associated diabetic complications such as peripheral vascular or circulatory problems, code 250.7x.
640-641	PDX	Dehydration or Electrolyte Imbalance	Look for alternative or co-equal diagnosis as principal reason for admission: dehydration, electrolyte imbalance, hyponatremia, hypokalemia, etc. What was the "focus" of the admission? Are there criteria for acute renal failure?
919-921	PDX	Complication of insulin pump	If hyperglycemia is due to complication of insulin pump, code 996.57 would apply and assigned as PDX.
638	CC	Chronic Kidney Disease, Stage 4 or 5	Chronic Kidney Disease (CKD) is always codable, pertinent chronic condition. Very common in diabetes. GFR <30 = Stage 4; <15 = Stage 5.

Alt DRG	PDX / MCC-CC / Procedure		Tips
682-684	PDX	Acute renal failure / Acute Kidney Injury (AKI)	Look for AKI criteria. *See Key References – Acute Renal Failure.* Dehydration is most common cause of acute renal failure. Code acute renal failure first in the presence of dehydration even if only treatment is IV fluids. *Coding Clinic 2002 Q2 P21.*
291-293	PDX	CHF (4280) due to fluid overload	For patients with ESRD admitted for fluid overload from noncompliance with dialysis and CHF, CHF is assigned as PDX unless the provider specifically documents that the fluid overload is not due to CHF (CHF is not decompensated, fluid overload is non-cardiogenic) in which case fluid overload (276.69) is the PDX. *See Coding Clinic 2007 Q3 P9.*
643-645	PDX	SIADH (253.6)	Look for SIADH in patients with hyponatremia. Defined as excessive secretion of anti-diuretic hormone (ADH). Characterized by hyponatremia that does not improve with treatment, low serum osmolality and normal or elevated urine osmolality. RX: Fluid restriction, discontinue thiazide diuretics, hypertonic saline (3%) infusion if severe.

640-641 Nutritional, Metabolic, Fluids/Electrolyte Disorders (cont.)

Alt DRG	PDX / MCC-CC / Procedure		Tips
374 Various DRGs	PDX	Neoplasm as reason for admission	Dehydration or electrolyte imbalance would be coded as PDX if admitted and treated for this only. If admission also includes any workup, treatment, or staging of a malignancy, the malignancy can be sequenced as the PDX.

682-684 Renal Failure RW 1.5401 / 0.9655 / 0.6213

Alt DRG	PDX / MCC-CC / Procedure		Tips
871-872 280-285 193-195 Other DRGs	PDX	Verify reason for admission and/or underlying etiology	Verify reason for admission and/or underlying etiology of the acute renal failure (if not due to dehydration), such as sepsis, acute MI, pneumonia. Acute renal failure is a manifestation of organ failure in septic patients. Code acute renal failure first in the presence of dehydration even if only treatment is IV fluids.
673-675	PROC	Renal dialysis access	Dialysis AV shunt (39.27), peritoneal fistula (54.93), or revision or removal of renal dialysis shunt (39.42, 39.43).

689-690 Kidney & Urinary Tract Infections RW 1.1300 / 0.7693

Alt DRG	PDX / MCC-CC / Procedure		Tips
871-872	PDX	Sepsis (SIRS due to Infection)	Look for clinical criteria for sepsis – *See Key References - Sepsis.* Admission for a simple UTI is rarely necessary, unless sepsis or another complication is present.
70-71	PDX	Encephalopathy as primary reason for admission	Many patients with UTIs, especially the elderly, will have an altered mental status due to "metabolic encephalopathy". This would be the PDX if the primary reason for admission, e.g., the UTI could have been treated as an outpatient or the "focus" of admission is mainly the altered mental status. UTI would be assigned as CC.
698-700	PDX	Infection due to Foley (996.64) or other catheter	Must be specifically documented by the physician that the infection is "due to" the catheter or device. If not documented, a query to clarify is recommended.

695-696 Kidney & Urinary Tract Signs & Symptoms RW 1.2773 / 0.6615

Alt DRG	PDX / MCC-CC / Procedure		Tips
689-690 691-694 698-700 Other DRGs	PDX	More specific diagnosis as PDX: cystitis, UTI, urinary stones, etc.	Look for a more specific diagnosis rather than signs and symptoms. Signs and symptoms should not be used as a PDX if a possible/ probable or confirmed cause is present. Admission for these symptoms (urinary retention, hematuria, etc.) is rarely needed unless a more complicated diagnosis is present or a procedure was performed.

713-714 Transurethral Prostatectomy — RW 1.3814 / 0.7402

Alt DRG	PDX / MCC-CC / Procedure		Tips
665-667	PDX	Admission for acute urinary condition, such as UTI or other interrelated condition, as PDX	If patient was admitted with an acute UTI treated with antibiotics (or for another acute urinary condition) and subsequently had TURP for the BPH, the PDX would remain the UTI (or the other acute urinary condition), and the DRG assigned becomes "Prostatectomy". TURP for BPH is usually performed on an outpatient basis.
984-986	PDX	Post-operative condition or complication following outpatient surgery	Reason for admission (principal diagnosis) is a complication or other condition *following ambulatory surgery*, such as cardiac arrhythmia, etc. In these cases, the surgical diagnosis would be listed as a SDX and the surgical procedure also coded.

749-750 Other Female Reprod System OR Procedures — RW 2.6239 / 1.0854

Alt DRG	PDX / MCC-CC / Procedure		Tips
335-337	PDX	Abdominal adhesions (568.0)	Determine whether abdominal adhesions (5680) vs. female pelvic adhesions (6146) is PDX and reason for adhesiolysis.

811-812 Anemia RW 1.2488 / 0.7985

Alt DRG	PDX / MCC-CC / Procedure		Tips
377-379	PDX	GI bleeding as cause of anemia	Melena, hematochezia (rectal bleeding), hematemesis (vomiting blood), positive stool blood; monitoring of Hgb/Hct; NSAIDs (including aspirin) indicate anemia due to GI bleeding. RX: EGD/Colonoscopy performed or planned; Prilosec, antacids. Transfusion is treatment for both anemia and GI bleeding. Evaluation of anemia or GI blood loss in stable patients may often be conducted on an outpatient basis.
813	PDX	Thrombocytopenia (287.4, 287.5)	If cancer / chemotherapy patients admitted for blood transfusion (due to anemia), look for platelet transfusion for thrombocytopenia as co-equal PDX. Platelet transfusion usually not necessary unless platelet count < 50,000.
374-376 Other DRGs	PDX	Colon cancer or other malignancy	Anemia would be coded as PDX if admitted and treated for the anemia only. If admission also includes any workup, treatment, or staging of a malignancy, the malignancy can be sequenced as the PDX. *See also Coding Guidelines – Neoplasms.*

813 Coagulation Disorders RW 1.6433

Alt DRG	PDX / MCC-CC / Procedure		Tips
Other Medical DRGs	PDX	Verify PDX: codes 286.x should rarely be used	Do not assign codes from category 286, Coagulation Defects, for patients on anticoagulant therapy. Code the reason why the patient was admitted, such as, hematoma, bleeding, abnormal coagulation profile. If the reason for admission is adverse effect of Coumadin with elevated INR/PT only, assign codes 790.92 (abnormal coagulation profile) and E934.2. If taken improperly (a poisoning), assign code 964.2 as PDX.

846-848 Chemotherapy w/o Acute Leukemia as SDX RW 2.4377 / 1.1062 / 0.8635

Alt DRG	PDX / MCC-CC / Procedure		Tips
Neoplasm DRGs	PDX	Malignancy as reason for admission	Determine whether the sole purpose for the admission was for administration of chemotherapy (V58.11). If chemotherapy was not the sole reason for the admission but was also for workup, staging, or other treatment of cancer, the malignancy could be sequenced as the PDX. *See also Coding Clinic 1994, Q3, P13 and Coding Guidelines – Neoplasms.*

864 Fever RW 0.8441

Alt DRG	PDX / MCC-CC / Procedure		Tips
871-872	PDX	Sepsis (SIRS due to Infection)	Look for sepsis criteria in addition to fever: WBC, Pulse, Respirations, others. Need some indication that infection is the likely cause, but does not require a specific localized infection. RX IV antibiotics. *See Key References – Sepsis.*
862-863	PDX	Postop infection	Admitted for possible infection causing fever following a surgical procedure, such as prostate biopsy. Look for sepsis criteria in addition to fever: increased WBC, pulse, respirations, others (see above). RX IV antibiotics.
867-869 Other DRGs	PDX	Etiology of fever, or "probable infectious cause" of fever	Fever (including "fever of unknown origin") is a symptom code (780.60) and not assigned if explained by an underlying cause, especially infection. Look for any indicators of a cause or possible/ suspected cause of fever as a query opportunity. If no specific infection is identified and physician documentation indicates that an infection was suspected and treated (IV antibiotics), code to "probable infection" 136.9. A diagnosis of "culture-negative bacterial infection" is coded to 041.9.

864 Fever (cont.)

Alt DRG	PDX / MCC-CC / Procedure		Tips
865-866	PDX	Viral illness as etiology of fever	Unspecified viral syndrome, code 079.9, would be used only when the type of virus has not been identified by laboratory tests and only when the symptom complex has not been identified, such as that of influenza (487.1), viral hepatitis (070.9), etc. Viral syndrome with associated diarrhea is assigned 008.8, viral enteritis NOS. *See Coding Clinic 1987, Jan-Feb.*

871-872 Sepsis w/o Vent 96+ Hrs RW 1.8527 / 1.0687

Alt DRG	PDX / MCC-CC / Procedure		Tips
94	PDX	Meningitis as an interrelated PDX with sepsis	Most cases of meningitis are caused by bacteria or viruses that enter the bloodstream via the upper respiratory tract and then infect the meninges of the brain. Meningitis is not typically a localized infection that progresses to sepsis. Bacteremia or septicemia, when it occurs, usually precedes the meningitis. Because there is no underlying/ localized infection, the two may be considered interrelated & either sequenced as PDX, although meningitis is likely to be the focus of the admission.
314	PDX	Sepsis "due to" device, implant, graft	Code a complication code (e.g., 996.62, 996.73) as PDX if documented specifically as "due to" (presence of) a device, implant or grafts.
853-855	PROC	Minor operative procedure	Evidence of an operative procedure performed in a patient with sepsis, such as excisional debridement (86.22), transbronchial biopsy (33.27), or other significant procedure.
870	Other	Duration of mechanical ventilation 96+ hrs	If patient on ventilator, follow and calculate duration carefully if longer than 3 days. DRG changes if duration 96+ hours. *See Key References – Mechanical Ventilation* for calculation rules.

880 Acute Adjust Reaction & Psychosocial Dysfunction — RW 0.6388

Alt DRG	PDX / MCC-CC / Procedure		Tips
884	PDX	Dementia or Organic Disturbances	Determine if acute anxiety, confusion, delirium, or hallucinations were possibly due to organic disturbances such as: Organic brain syndrome (310.9), presenile/senile dementia (290.x), fronto-temporal dementia (331.19). RX: Anti-psychotics like Zyprexa or Geodon, or Aricept, Cognex, etc.

881 / 882 Depressive Neuroses / Neuroses Except Depressive — RW 0.6541 / 0.6953

Alt DRG	PDX / MCC-CC / Procedure		Tips
885	PDX	Verify principal diagnosis	Look for schizophrenic disorder or other psychosis as reason for admission.

896-897 Alcohol/Drug Abuse or Dependence w/o Rehab Therapy — RW 1.5146 / 0.6824

Alt DRG	PDX / MCC-CC / Procedure		Tips
895	PROC	Rehab or detox (94.6x)	Alcohol or drug rehab and/or detoxification provided (94.6x).

917-918 Poisoning & Toxic Effect of Drugs RW 1.4093 / 0.6346

Alt DRG	PDX / MCC-CC / Procedure		Tips
Multiple DRGs	PDX	Confirm principal diagnosis is poisoning	Review condition or reaction to determine if an adverse effect or poisoning. Poisoning includes wrong person, dose, substance, route of administration; combination with alcohol, overdose, and toxicity due to a non-medicinal chemical substance. Poisoning code sequenced first. Adverse effect (including allergic) is a reaction to a therapeutic substance correctly administered. If adverse effect, then assign the manifestation as the PDX, which may include hypotension, arrhythmia, bleeding, acute renal failure, hepatitis, rash, anaphylaxis, encephalopathy, etc. *See also Coding Guidelines – Poisoning*

919-921 Complications of Treatment RW 1.7206 / 0.9779 / 0.6522

Alt DRG	PDX / MCC-CC / Procedure		Tips
Multiple DRGs	PDX	Confirm principal diagnosis is a complication	Complications of treatment should be PDX only when the patient is readmitted for a complication following prior surgery or other medical care. Cause / effect should be confirmed by physician documentation. Complications of care should be unexpected and unusual occurrences, not something that happens frequently following surgery, is expected, or is intrinsically/routinely associated with a procedure. Adverse effects, progression of disease, or post-op conditions attributable to the reason for the procedure or to other conditions are not complications of care. *See Coding Guidelines – Complications of Care* If admitted immediately following an outpatient procedure, assign the complication (or other reason for admission) as PDX. The condition for which the procedure was performed will be a SDX, and the surgical procedure would also be coded.

947-948 Signs & Symptoms — RW 1.1324 / 0.6897

Alt DRG	PDX / MCC-CC / Procedure		Tips
Medical DRGs	PDX	Look for cause or possible cause of symptoms, or other reasons for admission.	These DRGs include malaise, fatigue, mental status changes and others that are all symptom codes. Symptom code 789.5x (Ascites) is commonly caused by cirrhosis, malignancy, heart failure – code first the cause. Do not code symptoms when more specific underlying (or probable) conditions are present. *See Coding Guidelines – Signs and Symptoms.* Patient should have "unstable" vital signs, abnormal lab or other significant clinical problems to meet criteria for inpatient admission.

977 HIV with or w/o Other Related Condition — RW 1.1194

Alt DRG	PDX / MCC-CC / Procedure		Tips
974-976	Major Related Condition	Addition of HIV Major Related Condition	The following medical conditions as principal or secondary diagnosis (not a complete list): Sepsis; Herpes zoster/simplex Candidiasis; Thrush Pneumonia; Psychosis Organic brain syndrome; Encephalopathy Others

981-983 Extensive OR Procedure Unrelated to PDX RW 4.9319 / 2.8504 / 1.7462

Alt DRG	PDX / MCC-CC / Procedure		Tips
Multiple surgical DRGs	PDX	Diagnosis “related” to the surgical procedure as PDX	Review the medical record to determine whether or not the medical condition (or symptoms of the condition) associated with the principal surgical procedure was present on admission and could possibly meet the definition of principal diagnosis. These DRGs should be infrequently assigned.

987-988 Non-Extensive OR Procedure Unrelated to PDX RW 3.3422 / 1.7554

Alt DRG	PDX / MCC-CC / Procedure		Tips
Other surgical DRGs	PDX	Diagnosis “related” to the surgical procedure	Most of the procedures included in these DRGs are performed on an outpatient basis. If the patient was admitted following an outpatient procedure for a complication or other unrelated condition, the condition or complication code would be PDX resulting in the correct assignment of one of these DRGs. If the patient was not admitted following outpatient surgery, review the medical record to determine whether or not the medical condition (or symptoms of the condition) associated with the procedure was present on admission and could possibly meet the definition of principal diagnosis. These DRGs should be infrequently assigned.

DRG		MS-DRG Title	Weight	*GMLOS*
1	S	Heart transplant or implant of heart assist system w MCC	25.3518	*28.3*
2	S	Heart transplant or implant of heart assist system w/o MCC	15.2738	*15.9*
3	S*	ECMO or trach w MV 96+ hrs or PDX exc face, mouth, neck w major O.R.	17.6369	*27.2*
4	S*	Trach w MV 96+ hrs or PDX exc face, mouth & neck w/o major O.R.	10.9288	*20.3*
5	S	Liver transplant w MCC or intestinal transplant	10.4214	*15.1*
6	S	Liver transplant w/o MCC	4.7639	*7.9*
7	S	Lung transplant	9.1929	*15.4*
8	S	Simultaneous pancreas/kidney transplant	5.1527	*9.5*
10	S	Pancreas transplant	4.1554	*8.8*
11	S	Tracheostomy for face, mouth & neck diagnoses w MCC	4.7246	*11.4*
12	S	Tracheostomy for face, mouth & neck diagnoses w CC	3.2291	*8.3*
13	S	Tracheostomy for face, mouth & neck diagnoses w/o CC/MCC	2.1647	*5.7*
14	S	Allogeneic Bone Marrow Transplant	10.6157	*20.7*
16	S	Autologous Bone Marrow Transplant w CC/MCC	6.0304	*18.1*
17	S	Autologous Bone Marrow Transplant w/o CC/MCC	4.2906	*9.9*
20	S	Intracranial vascular procedures w PDX hemorrhage w MCC	9.3897	*14.3*
21	S	Intracranial vascular procedures w PDX hemorrhage w CC	6.4458	*11.9*
22	S	Intracranial vascular procedures w PDX hemorrhage w/o CC/MCC	4.7113	*5.5*
23	S*	Cranio w major dev impl/acute complx CNS PDX w MCC or chemo implt	5.1587	*8.0*

DRG		MS-DRG Title	Weight	*GMLOS*
24	S*	Cranio w major dev impl/acute complx CNS PDX w/o MCC	3.7121	*4.5*
25	S*	Craniotomy & endovascular intracranial procedures w MCC	4.4422	*7.8*
26	S*	Craniotomy & endovascular intracranial procedures w CC	2.9842	*5.0*
27	S*	Craniotomy & endovascular intracranial procedures w/o CC/MCC	2.2505	*2.6*
28	S*	Spinal procedures w MCC	5.4339	*9.6*
29	S*	Spinal procedures w CC or spinal neurostimulators	3.0782	*4.6*
30	S*	Spinal procedures w/o CC/MCC	1.8091	*2.5*
31	S*	Ventricular shunt procedures w MCC	3.9460	*7.7*
32	S*	Ventricular shunt procedures w CC	1.9780	*3.4*
33	S*	Ventricular shunt procedures w/o CC/MCC	1.5226	*2.0*
34	S	Carotid artery stent procedure w MCC	3.4145	*4.7*
35	S	Carotid artery stent procedure w CC	2.1781	*2.1*
36	S	Carotid artery stent procedure w/o CC/MCC	1.7224	*1.3*
37	S	Extracranial procedures w MCC	3.0641	*5.5*
38	S	Extracranial procedures w CC	1.5958	*2.4*
39	S	Extracranial procedures w/o CC/MCC	1.0452	*1.4*
40	S*	Periph/cranial nerve & other nerv syst proc w MCC	3.7851	*8.3*
41	S*	Periph/cranial nerve & other nerv syst proc w CC or periph neurostim	2.1731	*5.0*
42	S*	Periph/cranial nerve & other nerv syst proc w/o CC/MCC	1.8616	*2.6*

DRG		MS-DRG Title	Weight	*GMLOS*
52	M	Spinal disorders & injuries w CC/MCC	1.4102	*4.0*
53	M	Spinal disorders & injuries w/o CC/MCC	0.8746	*2.7*
54	M*	Nervous system neoplasms w MCC	1.3195	*4.1*
55	M*	Nervous system neoplasms w/o MCC	1.0100	*3.1*
56	M*	Degenerative nervous system disorders w MCC	1.7368	*5.3*
57	M*	Degenerative nervous system disorders w/o MCC	0.9841	*3.6*
58	M	Multiple sclerosis & cerebellar ataxia w MCC	1.6027	*5.4*
59	M	Multiple sclerosis & cerebellar ataxia w CC	1.0399	*4.0*
60	M	Multiple sclerosis & cerebellar ataxia w/o CC/MCC	0.7899	*3.1*
61	M	Acute ischemic stroke w use of thrombolytic agent w MCC	2.7316	*5.8*
62	M	Acute ischemic stroke w use of thrombolytic agent w CC	1.8561	*4.2*
63	M	Acute ischemic stroke w use of thrombolytic agent w/o CC/MCC	1.4685	*3.0*
64	**M***	**Intracranial hemorrhage or cerebral infarction w MCC**	**1.7417**	***4.7***
65	**M***	**Intracranial hemorrhage or cerebral infarction w CC or TPA in 24 hrs**	**1.0776**	***3.5***
66	**M***	**Intracranial hemorrhage or cerebral infarction w/o CC/MCC**	**0.7566**	***2.5***
67	**M**	**Nonspecific CVA & precerebral occlusion w/o infarct w MCC**	**1.4172**	***4.1***
68	**M**	**Nonspecific CVA & precerebral occlusion w/o infarct w/o MCC**	**0.8582**	***2.5***
69	**M**	**Transient ischemia**	**0.6948**	***2.2***
70	M*	Nonspecific cerebrovascular disorders w MCC	1.6593	*4.9*

DRG		MS-DRG Title	Weight	*GMLOS*
71	M*	Nonspecific cerebrovascular disorders w CC	0.9796	*3.6*
72	M*	Nonspecific cerebrovascular disorders w/o CC/MCC	0.6919	*2.3*
73	M	Cranial & peripheral nerve disorders w MCC	1.3014	*3.9*
74	M	Cranial & peripheral nerve disorders w/o MCC	0.8786	*3.1*
75	M	Viral meningitis w CC/MCC	1.5918	*5.2*
76	M	Viral meningitis w/o CC/MCC	0.8425	*3.2*
77	M	Hypertensive encephalopathy w MCC	1.6290	*4.6*
78	M	Hypertensive encephalopathy w CC	0.9467	*3.1*
79	M	Hypertensive encephalopathy w/o CC/MCC	0.7118	*2.3*
80	M	Nontraumatic stupor & coma w MCC	1.2252	*3.7*
81	M	Nontraumatic stupor & coma w/o MCC	0.7455	*2.6*
82	M	Traumatic stupor & coma, coma >1 hr w MCC	1.9463	*3.4*
83	M	Traumatic stupor & coma, coma >1 hr w CC	1.2643	*3.4*
84	M	Traumatic stupor & coma, coma >1 hr w/o CC/MCC	0.8491	*2.1*
85	M*	Traumatic stupor & coma, coma <1 hr w MCC	1.9733	*4.9*
86	M*	Traumatic stupor & coma, coma <1 hr w CC	1.1105	*3.3*
87	M*	Traumatic stupor & coma, coma <1 hr w/o CC/MCC	0.7345	*2.2*
88	M	Concussion w MCC	1.5029	*3.9*
89	M	Concussion w CC	0.9406	*2.7*

DRG		MS-DRG Title	Weight	*GMLOS*
90	M	Concussion w/o CC/MCC	0.7140	*1.9*
91	M*	Other disorders of nervous system w MCC	1.5851	*4.3*
92	M*	Other disorders of nervous system w CC	0.8918	*3.1*
93	M*	Other disorders of nervous system w/o CC/MCC	0.6614	*2.2*
94	M	Bacterial & tuberculous infections of nervous system w MCC	3.4974	*8.3*
95	M	Bacterial & tuberculous infections of nervous system w CC	2.2787	*6.2*
96	M	Bacterial & tuberculous infections of nervous system w/o CC/MCC	1.9694	*4.5*
97	M	Non-bacterial infect of nervous sys exc viral meningitis w MCC	3.1963	*8.5*
98	M	Non-bacterial infect of nervous sys exc viral meningitis w CC	1.7657	*5.8*
99	M	Non-bacterial infect of nervous sys exc viral meningitis w/o CC/MCC	1.1835	*4.1*
100	M*	Seizures w MCC	1.5185	*4.2*
101	M*	Seizures w/o MCC	0.7569	*2.6*
102	M	Headaches w MCC	1.0430	*3.1*
103	M	Headaches w/o MCC	0.6663	*2.3*
113	S	Orbital procedures w CC/MCC	1.8998	*4.0*
114	S	Orbital procedures w/o CC/MCC	1.0216	*2.3*
115	S	Extraocular procedures except orbit	1.2543	*3.2*
116	S	Intraocular procedures w CC/MCC	1.4806	*3.2*
117	S	Intraocular procedures w/o CC/MCC	0.8211	*1.8*

DRG		MS-DRG Title	Weight	*GMLOS*
121	M	Acute major eye infections w CC/MCC	1.0215	*3.9*
122	M	Acute major eye infections w/o CC/MCC	0.6147	*2.9*
123	M	Neurological eye disorders	0.6963	*2.2*
124	M	Other disorders of the eye w MCC	1.1990	*3.7*
125	M	Other disorders of the eye w/o MCC	0.6812	*2.5*
129	S	Major head & neck procedures w CC/MCC or major device	2.1925	*3.6*
130	S	Major head & neck procedures w/o CC/MCC	1.2687	*2.1*
131	S	Cranial/facial procedures w CC/MCC	2.2038	*3.9*
132	S	Cranial/facial procedures w/o CC/MCC	1.2855	*2.0*
133	S	Other ear, nose, mouth & throat O.R. procedures w CC/MCC	1.7824	*3.6*
134	S	Other ear, nose, mouth & throat O.R. procedures w/o CC/MCC	0.9584	*1.8*
135	S	Sinus & mastoid procedures w CC/MCC	2.0110	*4.1*
136	S	Sinus & mastoid procedures w/o CC/MCC	0.9709	*1.8*
137	S	Mouth procedures w CC/MCC	1.3477	*3.7*
138	S	Mouth procedures w/o CC/MCC	0.8304	*2.0*
139	S	Salivary gland procedures	0.9169	*1.5*
146	M	Ear, nose, mouth & throat malignancy w MCC	2.0402	*5.6*
147	M	Ear, nose, mouth & throat malignancy w CC	1.2317	*3.9*
148	M	Ear, nose, mouth & throat malignancy w/o CC/MCC	0.7688	*2.3*

DRG		MS-DRG Title	Weight	*GMLOS*
149	M	Dysequilibrium	0.6184	*2.1*
150	M	Epistaxis w MCC	1.3298	*3.7*
151	M	Epistaxis w/o MCC	0.6557	*2.2*
152	M	Otitis media & URI w MCC	1.0042	*3.3*
153	M	Otitis media & URI w/o MCC	0.6439	*2.4*
154	M	Other ear, nose, mouth & throat diagnoses w MCC	1.3785	*4.1*
155	M	Other ear, nose, mouth & throat diagnoses w CC	0.8610	*3.1*
156	M	Other ear, nose, mouth & throat diagnoses w/o CC/MCC	0.6160	*2.3*
157	M	Dental & oral diseases w MCC	1.5380	*4.5*
158	M	Dental & oral diseases w CC	0.8525	*3.1*
159	M	Dental & oral diseases w/o CC/MCC	0.6100	*2.1*
163	S*	Major chest procedures w MCC	5.0952	*11.0*
164	S*	Major chest procedures w CC	2.6086	*5.6*
165	S*	Major chest procedures w/o CC/MCC	1.7943	*3.3*
166	S*	Other resp system O.R. procedures w MCC	3.6741	*8.8*
167	S*	Other resp system O.R. procedures w CC	1.9860	*5.2*
168	S*	Other resp system O.R. procedures w/o CC/MCC	1.3101	*3.0*
175	M*	Pulmonary embolism w MCC	1.5346	*5.3*
176	M*	Pulmonary embolism w/o MCC	0.9891	*3.7*

DRG		MS-DRG Title	Weight	*GMLOS*
177	**M***	**Respiratory infections & inflammations w MCC**	**1.9934**	***6.4***
178	**M***	**Respiratory infections & inflammations w CC**	**1.3955**	***5.1***
179	**M***	**Respiratory infections & inflammations w/o CC/MCC**	**0.9741**	***3.7***
180	M	Respiratory neoplasms w MCC	1.7026	*5.4*
181	M	Respiratory neoplasms w CC	1.1725	*3.8*
182	M	Respiratory neoplasms w/o CC/MCC	0.7905	*2.6*
183	M	Major chest trauma w MCC	1.4649	*4.8*
184	M	Major chest trauma w CC	0.9832	*3.4*
185	M	Major chest trauma w/o CC/MCC	0.6907	*2.5*
186	M*	Pleural effusion w MCC	1.5727	*4.9*
187	M*	Pleural effusion w CC	1.0808	*3.6*
188	M*	Pleural effusion w/o CC/MCC	0.7468	*2.6*
189	**M**	**Pulmonary edema & respiratory failure**	**1.2184**	***3.9***
190	**M***	**Chronic obstructive pulmonary disease w MCC**	**1.1708**	***4.2***
191	**M***	**Chronic obstructive pulmonary disease w CC**	**0.9343**	***3.5***
192	**M***	**Chronic obstructive pulmonary disease w/o CC/MCC**	**0.7120**	***2.8***
193	**M***	**Simple pneumonia & pleurisy w MCC**	**1.4550**	***5.0***
194	**M***	**Simple pneumonia & pleurisy w CC**	**0.9771**	***3.8***
195	**M***	**Simple pneumonia & pleurisy w/o CC/MCC**	**0.6997**	***2.9***

DRG		MS-DRG Title	Weight	*GMLOS*
196	M*	Interstitial lung disease w MCC	1.6686	*5.4*
197	M*	Interstitial lung disease w CC	1.0627	*3.8*
198	M*	Interstitial lung disease w/o CC/MCC	0.7958	*2.9*
199	M	Pneumothorax w MCC	1.8127	*5.9*
200	M	Pneumothorax w CC	0.9692	*3.3*
201	M	Pneumothorax w/o CC/MCC	0.7053	*2.6*
202	M	Bronchitis & asthma w CC/MCC	0.8678	*3.2*
203	M	Bronchitis & asthma w/o CC/MCC	0.6391	*2.5*
204	M	Respiratory signs & symptoms	0.6780	*2.1*
205	M*	Other respiratory system diagnoses w MCC	1.3935	*4.0*
206	M*	Other respiratory system diagnoses w/o MCC	0.7911	*2.5*
207	**M***	**Respiratory system diagnosis w ventilator support 96+ hours**	**5.2556**	***12.1***
208	**M**	**Respiratory system diagnosis w ventilator support <96 hours**	**2.2871**	***5.0***
215	S	Other heart assist system implant	14.7790	*10.0*
216	S*	Cardiac valve & oth maj cardiothoracic proc w card cath w MCC	9.4801	*13.1*
217	S*	Cardiac valve & oth maj cardiothoracic proc w card cath w CC	6.2835	*8.4*
218	S*	Cardiac valve & oth maj cardiothoracic proc w card cath w/o CC/MCC	5.4262	*6.1*
219	S*	Cardiac valve & oth maj cardiothoracic proc w/o card cath w MCC	7.9191	*10.0*
220	S*	Cardiac valve & oth maj cardiothoracic proc w/o card cath w CC	5.2917	*6.6*

DRG		MS-DRG Title	Weight	*GMLOS*
221	S*	Cardiac valve & oth maj cardiothoracic proc w/o card cath w/o CC/MCC	4.6424	*4.9*
222	S	Cardiac defib implant w cardiac cath w AMI/HF/shock w MCC	8.8167	*9.6*
223	S	Cardiac defib implant w cardiac cath w AMI/HF/shock w/o MCC	6.4257	*4.6*
224	S	Cardiac defib implant w cardiac cath w/o AMI/HF/shock w MCC	7.7224	*8.1*
225	S	Cardiac defib implant w cardiac cath w/o AMI/HF/shock w/o MCC	5.9206	*4.1*
226	S	Cardiac defibrillator implant w/o cardiac cath w MCC	7.0099	*6.0*
227	S	Cardiac defibrillator implant w/o cardiac cath w/o MCC	5.5397	*2.2*
228	S	Other cardiothoracic procedures w MCC	6.8682	*11.1*
229	S	Other cardiothoracic procedures w CC	4.4413	*6.9*
230	S	Other cardiothoracic procedures w/o CC/MCC	3.6669	*4.4*
231	S	Coronary bypass w PTCA w MCC	7.8158	*10.7*
232	S	Coronary bypass w PTCA w/o MCC	5.6145	*8.1*
233	S*	Coronary bypass w cardiac cath w MCC	7.3887	*11.9*
234	S*	Coronary bypass w cardiac cath w/o MCC	4.8270	*8.0*
235	S*	Coronary bypass w/o cardiac cath w MCC	5.8478	*9.2*
236	S*	Coronary bypass w/o cardiac cath w/o MCC	3.8011	*6.0*
237	S	Major cardiovascular procedures w MCC	5.0962	*6.9*
238	S	Major cardiovascular procedures w/o MCC	3.3576	*2.6*
239	S*	Amputation for circ sys disorders exc upper limb & toe w MCC	4.8601	*10.9*

DRG		MS-DRG Title	Weight	*GMLOS*
240	S*	Amputation for circ sys disorders exc upper limb & toe w CC	2.6789	*7.2*
241	S*	Amputation for circ sys disorders exc upper limb & toe w/o CC/MCC	1.4226	*4.6*
242	S*	Permanent cardiac pacemaker implant w MCC	3.7491	*5.9*
243	S*	Permanent cardiac pacemaker implant w CC	2.6716	*3.7*
244	S*	Permanent cardiac pacemaker implant w/o CC/MCC	2.1608	*2.4*
245	S	AICD generator procedures	4.7022	*3.3*
246	S	Perc cardiovasc proc w drug-eluting stent w MCC or 4+ vessels/stents	3.1830	*3.9*
247	S	Perc cardiovasc proc w drug-eluting stent w/o MCC	2.0408	*2.1*
248	S	Perc cardiovasc proc w non-drug-eluting stent w MCC or 4+ ves/stents	2.9479	*4.6*
249	S	Perc cardiovasc proc w non-drug-eluting stent w/o MCC	1.8245	*2.4*
250	S	Perc cardiovasc proc w/o coronary artery stent w MCC	2.9881	*5.1*
251	S	Perc cardiovasc proc w/o coronary artery stent w/o MCC	1.9737	*2.4*
252	S	Other vascular procedures w MCC	3.1477	*5.3*
253	S	Other vascular procedures w CC	2.5172	*4.1*
254	S	Other vascular procedures w/o CC/MCC	1.7012	*2.2*
255	S*	Upper limb & toe amputation for circ system disorders w MCC	2.6404	*6.8*
256	S*	Upper limb & toe amputation for circ system disorders w CC	1.5973	*5.3*
257	S*	Upper limb & toe amputation for circ system disorders w/o CC/MCC	0.9017	*3.0*
258	S	Cardiac pacemaker device replacement w MCC	2.7229	*4.9*

DRG		MS-DRG Title	Weight	*GMLOS*
259	S	Cardiac pacemaker device replacement w/o MCC	1.9462	*2.7*
260	S	Cardiac pacemaker revision except device replacement w MCC	3.7238	*7.7*
261	S	Cardiac pacemaker revision except device replacement w CC	1.7284	*3.2*
262	S	Cardiac pacemaker revision except device replacement w/o CC/MCC	1.3866	*2.3*
263	S	Vein ligation & stripping	1.8888	*3.6*
264	S*	Other circulatory system O.R. procedures	2.7138	*5.6*
265	S	AICD lead procedures	2.6890	*2.5*
280	**M***	**Acute myocardial infarction, discharged alive w MCC**	**1.7431**	***4.7***
281	**M***	**Acute myocardial infarction, discharged alive w CC**	**1.0568**	***3.1***
282	**M***	**Acute myocardial infarction, discharged alive w/o CC/MCC**	**0.7551**	***2.1***
283	M	Acute myocardial infarction, expired w MCC	1.6885	*3.0*
284	M	Acute myocardial infarction, expired w CC	0.7614	*1.8*
285	M	Acute myocardial infarction, expired w/o CC/MCC	0.5227	*1.4*
286	**M**	**Circulatory disorders except AMI, w card cath w MCC**	**2.1058**	***4.9***
287	**M**	**Circulatory disorders except AMI, w card cath w/o MCC**	**1.0866**	***2.4***
288	M*	Acute & subacute endocarditis w MCC	2.7956	*7.8*
289	M*	Acute & subacute endocarditis w CC	1.7891	*5.7*
290	M*	Acute & subacute endocarditis w/o CC/MCC	1.2359	*3.9*
291	**M***	**Heart failure & shock w MCC**	**1.5031**	***4.6***

DRG		MS-DRG Title	Weight	*GMLOS*
292	**M***	**Heart failure & shock w CC**	**0.9938**	***3.7***
293	**M***	**Heart failure & shock w/o CC/MCC**	**0.6723**	***2.6***
294	M	Deep vein thrombophlebitis w CC/MCC	0.9439	*4.0*
295	M	Deep vein thrombophlebitis w/o CC/MCC	0.6287	*3.1*
296	M	Cardiac arrest, unexplained w MCC	1.3013	*1.9*
297	M	Cardiac arrest, unexplained w CC	0.6063	*1.2*
298	M	Cardiac arrest, unexplained w/o CC/MCC	0.4260	*1.0*
299	M*	Peripheral vascular disorders w MCC	1.3647	*4.4*
300	M*	Peripheral vascular disorders w CC	0.9666	*3.6*
301	M*	Peripheral vascular disorders w/o CC/MCC	0.6681	*2.7*
302	M	Atherosclerosis w MCC	1.0287	*2.9*
303	M	Atherosclerosis w/o MCC	0.6034	*1.9*
304	M	Hypertension w MCC	1.0268	*3.3*
305	M	Hypertension w/o MCC	0.6176	*2.1*
306	M	Cardiac congenital & valvular disorders w MCC	1.3659	*3.9*
307	M	Cardiac congenital & valvular disorders w/o MCC	0.7917	*2.6*
308	**M**	**Cardiac arrhythmia & conduction disorders w MCC**	**1.2088**	***3.8***
309	**M**	**Cardiac arrhythmia & conduction disorders w CC**	**0.7867**	***2.7***
310	**M**	**Cardiac arrhythmia & conduction disorders w/o CC/MCC**	**0.5512**	***1.9***

DRG		MS-DRG Title	Weight	*GMLOS*
311	M	Angina pectoris	0.5649	*1.8*
312	**M**	**Syncope & collapse**	**0.7228**	***2.4***
313	**M**	**Chest pain**	**0.5992**	***1.8***
314	M*	Other circulatory system diagnoses w MCC	1.8941	*4.9*
315	M*	Other circulatory system diagnoses w CC	0.9534	*3.1*
316	M*	Other circulatory system diagnoses w/o CC/MCC	0.6358	*2.0*
326	S*	Stomach, esophageal & duodenal proc w MCC	5.6013	*11.6*
327	S*	Stomach, esophageal & duodenal proc w CC	2.6598	*6.1*
328	S*	Stomach, esophageal & duodenal proc w/o CC/MCC	1.4765	*2.6*
329	S*	Major small & large bowel procedures w MCC	5.1272	*11.9*
330	S*	Major small & large bowel procedures w CC	2.5609	*7.3*
331	S*	Major small & large bowel procedures w/o CC/MCC	1.6380	*4.4*
332	S*	Rectal resection w MCC	4.7072	*10.9*
333	S*	Rectal resection w CC	2.4466	*6.4*
334	S*	Rectal resection w/o CC/MCC	1.5849	*3.7*
335	S*	Peritoneal adhesiolysis w MCC	4.1615	*10.7*
336	S*	Peritoneal adhesiolysis w CC	2.3513	*7.0*
337	S*	Peritoneal adhesiolysis w/o CC/MCC	1.5742	*4.1*
338	S	Appendectomy w complicated principal diag w MCC	3.1217	*7.8*

DRG		MS-DRG Title	Weight	*GMLOS*
339	S	Appendectomy w complicated principal diag w CC	1.7117	*5.1*
340	S	Appendectomy w complicated principal diag w/o CC/MCC	1.1741	*3.0*
341	S	Appendectomy w/o complicated principal diag w MCC	2.1821	*4.6*
342	S	Appendectomy w/o complicated principal diag w CC	1.2968	*2.8*
343	S	Appendectomy w/o complicated principal diag w/o CC/MCC	0.9358	*1.6*
344	S	Minor small & large bowel procedures w MCC	3.5966	*8.9*
345	S	Minor small & large bowel procedures w CC	1.6865	*5.5*
346	S	Minor small & large bowel procedures w/o CC/MCC	1.2174	*4.0*
347	S	Anal & stomal procedures w MCC	2.5182	*6.3*
348	S	Anal & stomal procedures w CC	1.3585	*4.0*
349	S	Anal & stomal procedures w/o CC/MCC	0.8834	*2.4*
350	S	Inguinal & femoral hernia procedures w MCC	2.4598	*5.8*
351	S	Inguinal & femoral hernia procedures w CC	1.3761	*3.5*
352	S	Inguinal & femoral hernia procedures w/o CC/MCC	0.9239	*2.0*
353	S	Hernia procedures except inguinal & femoral w MCC	2.7885	*6.2*
354	S	Hernia procedures except inguinal & femoral w CC	1.6401	*4.0*
355	S	Hernia procedures except inguinal & femoral w/o CC/MCC	1.1783	*2.5*
356	S*	Other digestive system O.R. procedures w MCC	3.8388	*8.6*
357	S*	Other digestive system O.R. procedures w CC	2.1448	*5.4*

DRG		MS-DRG Title	Weight	*GMLOS*
358	S*	Other digestive system O.R. procedures w/o CC/MCC	1.3942	*3.2*
368	M	Major esophageal disorders w MCC	1.8779	*5.0*
369	M	Major esophageal disorders w CC	1.0660	*3.5*
370	M	Major esophageal disorders w/o CC/MCC	0.7486	*2.5*
371	**M***	**Major GI disorders & peritoneal infections w MCC**	**1.9027**	***6.2***
372	**M***	**Major GI disorders & peritoneal infections w CC**	**1.1733**	***4.8***
373	**M***	**Major GI disorders & peritoneal infections w/o CC/MCC**	**0.8103**	***3.6***
374	M*	Digestive malignancy w MCC	2.1051	*6.2*
375	M*	Digestive malignancy w CC	1.2561	*4.2*
376	M*	Digestive malignancy w/o CC/MCC	0.8738	*2.7*
377	**M***	**G.I. hemorrhage w MCC**	**1.7629**	***4.8***
378	**M***	**G.I. hemorrhage w CC**	**1.0029**	***3.3***
379	**M***	**G.I. hemorrhage w/o CC/MCC**	**0.6937**	***2.4***
380	M*	Complicated peptic ulcer w MCC	1.9223	*5.5*
381	M*	Complicated peptic ulcer w CC	1.1199	*3.8*
382	M*	Complicated peptic ulcer w/o CC/MCC	0.7784	*2.7*
383	M	Uncomplicated peptic ulcer w MCC	1.3850	*4.4*
384	M	Uncomplicated peptic ulcer w/o MCC	0.8501	*3.0*
385	M	Inflammatory bowel disease w MCC	1.7973	*6.0*

DRG		MS-DRG Title	Weight	*GMLOS*
386	M	Inflammatory bowel disease w CC	1.0097	*4.0*
387	M	Inflammatory bowel disease w/o CC/MCC	0.7533	*3.1*
388	M*	G.I. obstruction w MCC	1.6170	*5.3*
389	M*	G.I. obstruction w CC	0.8853	*3.6*
390	M*	G.I. obstruction w/o CC/MCC	0.6046	*2.7*
391	**M**	**Esophagitis, gastroent & misc digest disorders w MCC**	**1.1903**	***3.9***
392	**M**	**Esophagitis, gastroent & misc digest disorders w/o MCC**	**0.7395**	***2.9***
393	M	Other digestive system diagnoses w MCC	1.6563	*4.7*
394	M	Other digestive system diagnoses w CC	0.9653	*3.5*
395	M	Other digestive system diagnoses w/o CC/MCC	0.6669	*2.4*
405	S*	Pancreas, liver & shunt procedures w MCC	5.4333	*11.0*
406	S*	Pancreas, liver & shunt procedures w CC	2.7667	*6.0*
407	S*	Pancreas, liver & shunt procedures w/o CC/MCC	1.9139	*4.2*
408	S	Biliary tract proc except only cholecyst w or w/o c.d.e. w MCC	4.1182	*10.6*
409	S	Biliary tract proc except only cholecyst w or w/o c.d.e. w CC	2.4337	*6.7*
410	S	Biliary tract proc except only cholecyst w or w/o c.d.e. w/o CC/MCC	1.5123	*4.3*
411	S	Cholecystectomy w c.d.e. w MCC	3.5968	*9.3*
412	S	Cholecystectomy w c.d.e. w CC	2.3659	*6.5*
413	S	Cholecystectomy w c.d.e. w/o CC/MCC	1.7220	*4.2*

DRG		MS-DRG Title	Weight	*GMLOS*
414	S*	Cholecystectomy except by laparoscope w/o c.d.e. w MCC	3.6208	*8.8*
415	S*	Cholecystectomy except by laparoscope w/o c.d.e. w CC	2.0173	*5.8*
416	S*	Cholecystectomy except by laparoscope w/o c.d.e. w/o CC/MCC	1.3268	*3.5*
417	S	Laparoscopic cholecystectomy w/o c.d.e. w MCC	2.4784	*6.0*
418	S	Laparoscopic cholecystectomy w/o c.d.e. w CC	1.6536	*4.1*
419	S	Laparoscopic cholecystectomy w/o c.d.e. w/o CC/MCC	1.2239	*2.6*
420	S	Hepatobiliary diagnostic procedures w MCC	3.6786	*8.7*
421	S	Hepatobiliary diagnostic procedures w CC	1.7714	*4.6*
422	S	Hepatobiliary diagnostic procedures w/o CC/MCC	1.2175	*3.1*
423	S	Other hepatobiliary or pancreas O.R. procedures w MCC	4.2183	*9.6*
424	S	Other hepatobiliary or pancreas O.R. procedures w CC	2.3149	*6.3*
425	S	Other hepatobiliary or pancreas O.R. procedures w/o CC/MCC	1.6396	*3.8*
432	M	Cirrhosis & alcoholic hepatitis w MCC	1.7150	*4.7*
433	M	Cirrhosis & alcoholic hepatitis w CC	0.9249	*3.3*
434	M	Cirrhosis & alcoholic hepatitis w/o CC/MCC	0.6156	*2.4*
435	M	Malignancy of hepatobiliary system or pancreas w MCC	1.7356	*5.2*
436	M	Malignancy of hepatobiliary system or pancreas w CC	1.1548	*3.9*
437	M	Malignancy of hepatobiliary system or pancreas w/o CC/MCC	0.9282	*2.8*
438	M	Disorders of pancreas except malignancy w MCC	1.7210	*5.1*

DRG		MS-DRG Title	Weight	*GMLOS*
439	M	Disorders of pancreas except malignancy w CC	0.9162	*3.6*
440	M	Disorders of pancreas except malignancy w/o CC/MCC	0.6452	*2.7*
441	M*	Disorders of liver except malig,cirr,alc hepa w MCC	1.8534	*5.0*
442	M*	Disorders of liver except malig,cirr,alc hepa w CC	0.9280	*3.4*
443	M*	Disorders of liver except malig,cirr,alc hepa w/o CC/MCC	0.6418	*2.6*
444	M	Disorders of the biliary tract w MCC	1.6060	*4.7*
445	M	Disorders of the biliary tract w CC	1.0476	*3.4*
446	M	Disorders of the biliary tract w/o CC/MCC	0.7499	*2.4*
453	S	Combined anterior/posterior spinal fusion w MCC	11.7453	*9.7*
454	S	Combined anterior/posterior spinal fusion w CC	8.0200	*5.1*
455	S	Combined anterior/posterior spinal fusion w/o CC/MCC	6.2882	*3.1*
456	S	Spinal fus exc cerv w spinal curv/malig/infec or 9+ fus w MCC	9.5871	*10.2*
457	S	Spinal fus exc cerv w spinal curv/malig/infec or 9+ fus w CC	6.8188	*5.6*
458	S	Spinal fus exc cerv w spinal curv/malig/infec or 9+ fus w/o CC/MCC	5.1378	*3.3*
459	S*	Spinal fusion except cervical w MCC	6.8163	*7.1*
460	S*	Spinal fusion except cervical w/o MCC	4.0221	*3.1*
461	S	Bilateral or multiple major joint procs of lower extremity w MCC	5.0254	*6.1*
462	S	Bilateral or multiple major joint procs of lower extremity w/o MCC	3.5190	*3.5*
463	S*	Wnd debrid & skn grft exc hand for musculo-conn tiss dis w MCC	5.1152	*10.4*

DRG		MS-DRG Title	Weight	*GMLOS*
464	S*	Wnd debrid & skn grft exc hand for musculo-conn tiss dis w CC	3.0243	*6.2*
465	S*	Wnd debrid & skn grft exc hand for musculo-conn tiss dis w/o CC/MCC	1.9199	*3.8*
466	S*	Revision of hip or knee replacement w MCC	5.2748	*7.0*
467	S*	Revision of hip or knee replacement w CC	3.4140	*3.9*
468	S*	Revision of hip or knee replacement w/o CC/MCC	2.7624	*3.0*
469	**S***	**Major joint replacement or reattachment of lower extrem w MCC**	**3.4377**	***6.2***
470	**S***	**Major joint replacement or reattachment of lower extrem w/o MCC**	**2.1463**	***3.1***
471	S	Cervical spinal fusion w MCC	4.9444	*6.4*
472	S	Cervical spinal fusion w CC	2.9288	*2.5*
473	S	Cervical spinal fusion w/o CC/MCC	2.2458	*1.5*
474	S*	Amputation for musculoskeletal sys & conn tissue dis w MCC	3.6884	*8.8*
475	S*	Amputation for musculoskeletal sys & conn tissue dis w CC	2.0488	*5.7*
476	S*	Amputation for musculoskeletal sys & conn tissue dis w/o CC/MCC	1.0717	*3.1*
477	S*	Biopsies of musculoskeletal system & connective tissue w MCC	3.2827	*8.6*
478	S*	Biopsies of musculoskeletal system & connective tissue w CC	2.2115	*5.4*
479	S*	Biopsies of musculoskeletal system & connective tissue w/o CC/MCC	1.7340	*3.3*
480	S*	Hip & femur procedures except major joint w MCC	3.0694	*7.1*
481	S*	Hip & femur procedures except major joint w CC	1.9721	*4.8*
482	S*	Hip & femur procedures except major joint w/o CC/MCC	1.6305	*3.9*

DRG		MS-DRG Title	Weight	*GMLOS*
483	S*	Major joint & limb reattachment proc of upper extremity w CC/MCC	2.6488	*2.8*
484	S*	Major joint & limb reattachment proc of upper extremity w/o CC/MCC	2.2298	*1.8*
485	S	Knee procedures w pdx of infection w MCC	3.2719	*8.4*
486	S	Knee procedures w pdx of infection w CC	2.0199	*5.6*
487	S	Knee procedures w pdx of infection w/o CC/MCC	1.5215	*4.1*
488	S*	Knee procedures w/o pdx of infection w CC/MCC	1.7379	*3.5*
489	S*	Knee procedures w/o pdx of infection w/o CC/MCC	1.2799	*2.5*
490	S	Back & neck proc exc spinal fusion w CC/MCC or disc device/neurostim	1.8845	*3.4*
491	S	Back & neck proc exc spinal fusion w/o CC/MCC	1.0893	*1.9*
492	S*	Lower extrem & humer proc except hip,foot,femur w MCC	3.1831	*6.4*
493	S*	Lower extrem & humer proc except hip,foot,femur w CC	1.9971	*4.0*
494	S*	Lower extrem & humer proc except hip,foot,femur w/o CC/MCC	1.5073	*2.7*
495	S*	Local excision & removal int fix devices exc hip & femur w MCC	2.9110	*7.2*
496	S*	Local excision & removal int fix devices exc hip & femur w CC	1.7290	*4.0*
497	S*	Local excision & removal int fix devices exc hip & femur w/o CC/MCC	1.1731	*2.1*
498	S	Local excision & removal int fix devices of hip & femur w CC/MCC	2.1924	*5.3*
499	S	Local excision & removal int fix devices of hip & femur w/o CC/MCC	0.9577	*2.1*
500	S*	Soft tissue procedures w MCC	3.0116	*7.3*

DRG		MS-DRG Title	Weight	*GMLOS*
501	S*	Soft tissue procedures w CC	1.5804	*4.4*
502	S*	Soft tissue procedures w/o CC/MCC	1.1277	*2.4*
503	S	Foot procedures w MCC	2.2584	*6.3*
504	S	Foot procedures w CC	1.6133	*4.9*
505	S	Foot procedures w/o CC/MCC	1.2072	*2.7*
506	S	Major thumb or joint procedures	1.2041	*2.9*
507	S	Major shoulder or elbow joint procedures w CC/MCC	1.9667	*4.1*
508	S	Major shoulder or elbow joint procedures w/o CC/MCC	1.3190	*2.0*
509	S	Arthroscopy	1.3245	*2.7*
510	S*	Shoulder,elbow or forearm proc,exc major joint proc w MCC	2.2717	*4.8*
511	S*	Shoulder,elbow or forearm proc,exc major joint proc w CC	1.5894	*3.2*
512	S*	Shoulder,elbow or forearm proc,exc major joint proc w/o CC/MCC	1.2266	*2.0*
513	S	Hand or wrist proc, except major thumb or joint proc w CC/MCC	1.4122	*3.7*
514	S	Hand or wrist proc, except major thumb or joint proc w/o CC/MCC	0.8781	*2.2*
515	S*	Other musculoskelet sys & conn tiss O.R. proc w MCC	3.3340	*7.5*
516	S*	Other musculoskelet sys & conn tiss O.R. proc w CC	2.0160	*4.5*
517	S*	Other musculoskelet sys & conn tiss O.R. proc w/o CC/MCC	1.6777	*2.8*
533	M*	Fractures of femur w MCC	1.3759	*4.3*
534	M*	Fractures of femur w/o MCC	0.7364	*2.9*

DRG		MS-DRG Title	Weight	*GMLOS*
535	M*	Fractures of hip & pelvis w MCC	1.3085	*4.2*
536	M*	Fractures of hip & pelvis w/o MCC	0.7091	*3.0*
537	M	Sprains, strains, & dislocations of hip, pelvis & thigh w CC/MCC	0.8604	*3.4*
538	M	Sprains, strains, & dislocations of hip, pelvis & thigh w/o CC/MCC	0.6870	*2.4*
539	M*	Osteomyelitis w MCC	1.8631	*6.2*
540	M*	Osteomyelitis w CC	1.3063	*4.9*
541	M*	Osteomyelitis w/o CC/MCC	0.9743	*3.6*
542	M*	**Pathological fxs & musc-skelet & conn tiss malig w MCC**	1.9451	*6.0*
543	**M***	**Pathological fxs & musc-skelet & conn tiss malig w CC**	**1.1267**	***4.2***
544	**M***	**Pathological fxs & musc-skelet & conn tiss malig w/o CC/MCC**	**0.7736**	***3.2***
545	M*	Connective tissue disorders w MCC	2.4445	*6.0*
546	M*	Connective tissue disorders w CC	1.1711	*4.0*
547	M*	Connective tissue disorders w/o CC/MCC	0.8061	*2.9*
548	M	Septic arthritis w MCC	1.7811	*5.9*
549	M	Septic arthritis w CC	1.1101	*4.3*
550	M	Septic arthritis w/o CC/MCC	0.8149	*3.1*
551	**M***	**Medical back problems w MCC**	**1.6317**	***5.0***
552	**M***	**Medical back problems w/o MCC**	**0.8467**	***3.2***
553	M	Bone diseases & arthropathies w MCC	1.2370	*4.4*

DRG		MS-DRG Title	Weight	*GMLOS*
554	M	Bone diseases & arthropathies w/o MCC	0.7181	*2.9*
555	M	Signs & symptoms of musculoskeletal system & conn tissue w MCC	1.1974	*3.7*
556	M	Signs & symptoms of musculoskeletal system & conn tissue w/o MCC	0.7066	*2.6*
557	M*	Tendonitis, myositis & bursitis w MCC	1.4756	*5.1*
558	M*	Tendonitis, myositis & bursitis w/o MCC	0.8337	*3.4*
559	M*	Aftercare, musculoskeletal system & connective tissue w MCC	1.8639	*5.0*
560	M*	Aftercare, musculoskeletal system & connective tissue w CC	1.0260	*3.4*
561	M*	Aftercare, musculoskeletal system & connective tissue w/o CC/MCC	0.6408	*2.0*
562	M*	Fx, sprn, strn & disl except femur, hip, pelvis & thigh w MCC	1.3528	*4.4*
563	M*	Fx, sprn, strn & disl except femur, hip, pelvis & thigh w/o MCC	0.7535	*3.0*
564	M	Other musculoskeletal sys & connective tissue diagnoses w MCC	1.4855	*4.5*
565	M	Other musculoskeletal sys & connective tissue diagnoses w CC	0.9281	*3.6*
566	M	Other musculoskeletal sys & connective tissue diagnoses w/o CC/MCC	0.6642	*2.6*
570	**S***	**Skin debridement w MCC**	**2.4154**	***7.2***
571	**S***	**Skin debridement w CC**	**1.4906**	***5.4***
572	**S***	**Skin debridement w/o CC/MCC**	**1.0077**	***3.8***
573	S*	Skin graft for skin ulcer or cellulitis w MCC	3.4623	*8.2*
574	S*	Skin graft for skin ulcer or cellulitis w CC	2.6883	*7.1*
575	S*	Skin graft for skin ulcer or cellulitis w/o CC/MCC	1.4376	*4.2*

DRG		MS-DRG Title	Weight	*GMLOS*
576	S	Skin graft except for skin ulcer or cellulitis w MCC	4.2927	*7.9*
577	S	Skin graft except for skin ulcer or cellulitis w CC	2.0212	*4.0*
578	S	Skin graft except for skin ulcer or cellulitis w/o CC/MCC	1.2617	*2.4*
579	S*	Other skin, subcut tiss & breast proc w MCC	2.6106	*7.0*
580	S*	Other skin, subcut tiss & breast proc w CC	1.5398	*3.8*
581	S*	Other skin, subcut tiss & breast proc w/o CC/MCC	1.0605	*2.0*
582	S	Mastectomy for malignancy w CC/MCC	1.1913	*2.0*
583	S	Mastectomy for malignancy w/o CC/MCC	0.9711	*1.5*
584	S	Breast biopsy, local excision & other breast procedures w CC/MCC	1.6998	*3.5*
585	S	Breast biopsy, local excision & other breast procedures w/o CC/MCC	1.3162	*2.0*
592	M*	Skin ulcers w MCC	1.4131	*5.1*
593	M*	Skin ulcers w CC	1.0094	*4.2*
594	M*	Skin ulcers w/o CC/MCC	0.6814	*3.1*
595	M	Major skin disorders w MCC	1.9464	*5.7*
596	M	Major skin disorders w/o MCC	0.9284	*3.6*
597	M	Malignant breast disorders w MCC	1.7064	*5.2*
598	M	Malignant breast disorders w CC	1.0817	*3.9*
599	M	Malignant breast disorders w/o CC/MCC	0.6547	*2.5*
600	M	Non-malignant breast disorders w CC/MCC	0.9963	*3.8*

DRG		MS-DRG Title	Weight	*GMLOS*
601	M	Non-malignant breast disorders w/o CC/MCC	0.6445	*2.8*
602	**M***	**Cellulitis w MCC**	**1.4607**	***5.0***
603	**M***	**Cellulitis w/o MCC**	**0.8402**	***3.6***
604	M	Trauma to the skin, subcut tiss & breast w MCC	1.3223	*3.9*
605	M	Trauma to the skin, subcut tiss & breast w/o MCC	0.7372	*2.6*
606	M	Minor skin disorders w MCC	1.3594	*4.3*
607	M	Minor skin disorders w/o MCC	0.7043	*2.8*
614	S	Adrenal & pituitary procedures w CC/MCC	2.5455	*4.3*
615	S	Adrenal & pituitary procedures w/o CC/MCC	1.4579	*2.3*
616	S*	Amputat of lower limb for endocrine,nutrit,& metabol dis w MCC	4.0773	*10.9*
617	S*	Amputat of lower limb for endocrine,nutrit,& metabol dis w CC	2.0071	*6.1*
618	S*	Amputat of lower limb for endocrine,nutrit,& metabol dis w/o CC/MCC	1.2489	*4.3*
619	S	O.R. procedures for obesity w MCC	3.6200	*4.8*
620	S	O.R. procedures for obesity w CC	1.9399	*2.7*
621	S	O.R. procedures for obesity w/o CC/MCC	1.5772	*1.8*
622	S*	Skin grafts & wound debrid for endoc, nutrit & metab dis w MCC	3.3505	*9.1*
623	S*	Skin grafts & wound debrid for endoc, nutrit & metab dis w CC	1.8239	*5.7*
624	S*	Skin grafts & wound debrid for endoc, nutrit & metab dis w/o CC/MCC	0.9635	*3.5*
625	S	Thyroid, parathyroid & thyroglossal procedures w MCC	2.4009	*4.4*

DRG		MS-DRG Title	Weight	*GMLOS*
626	S	Thyroid, parathyroid & thyroglossal procedures w CC	1.2459	*2.0*
627	S	Thyroid, parathyroid & thyroglossal procedures w/o CC/MCC	0.8458	*1.3*
628	S*	Other endocrine, nutrit & metab O.R. proc w MCC	3.3515	*6.6*
629	S*	Other endocrine, nutrit & metab O.R. proc w CC	2.1292	*6.0*
630	S*	Other endocrine, nutrit & metab O.R. proc w/o CC/MCC	1.3444	*3.0*
637	M*	Diabetes w MCC	1.3888	*4.2*
638	M*	Diabetes w CC	0.8252	*3.0*
639	M*	Diabetes w/o CC/MCC	0.5708	*2.2*
640	**M***	**Misc Disorders of Nutrition, Metab, Fluids/Electrolytes w MCC**	**1.1111**	***3.3***
641	**M***	**Misc Disorders of Nutrition, Metab, Fluids/Electrolytes w/o MCC**	**0.6992**	***2.8***
642	M	Inborn and other disorders of metabolism	1.0674	*3.2*
643	M*	Endocrine disorders w MCC	1.6693	*5.5*
644	M*	Endocrine disorders w CC	1.0194	*3.9*
645	M*	Endocrine disorders w/o CC/MCC	0.7041	*2.8*
652	S	Kidney transplant	3.1530	*5.8*
653	S*	Major bladder procedures w MCC	5.9558	*12.7*
654	S*	Major bladder procedures w CC	3.0944	*7.8*
655	S*	Major bladder procedures w/o CC/MCC	2.1671	*4.7*
656	S	Kidney & ureter procedures for neoplasm w MCC	3.5221	*7.2*

DRG		MS-DRG Title	Weight	*GMLOS*
657	S	Kidney & ureter procedures for neoplasm w CC	2.0261	*4.5*
658	S	Kidney & ureter procedures for neoplasm w/o CC/MCC	1.5074	*2.8*
659	S*	Kidney & ureter procedures for non-neoplasm w MCC	3.4051	*7.6*
660	S*	Kidney & ureter procedures for non-neoplasm w CC	1.8827	*4.3*
661	S*	Kidney & ureter procedures for non-neoplasm w/o CC/MCC	1.3435	*2.3*
662	S	Minor bladder procedures w MCC	2.9801	*7.7*
663	S	Minor bladder procedures w CC	1.5666	*3.9*
664	S	Minor bladder procedures w/o CC/MCC	1.2208	*1.7*
665	S	Prostatectomy w MCC	3.1414	*9.2*
666	S	Prostatectomy w CC	1.7042	*4.5*
667	S	Prostatectomy w/o CC/MCC	0.8949	*2.0*
668	S	Transurethral procedures w MCC	2.5573	*6.6*
669	S	Transurethral procedures w CC	1.2693	*3.0*
670	S	Transurethral procedures w/o CC/MCC	0.8354	*1.9*
671	S	Urethral procedures w CC/MCC	1.5887	*4.3*
672	S	Urethral procedures w/o CC/MCC	0.8835	*1.9*
673	S	Other kidney & urinary tract procedures w MCC	3.1150	*6.5*
674	S	Other kidney & urinary tract procedures w CC	2.2378	*5.1*
675	S	Other kidney & urinary tract procedures w/o CC/MCC	1.3807	*1.9*

DRG		MS-DRG Title	Weight	*GMLOS*
682	**M***	**Renal failure w MCC**	**1.5401**	***4.7***
683	**M***	**Renal failure w CC**	**0.9655**	***3.7***
684	**M***	**Renal failure w/o CC/MCC**	**0.6213**	***2.5***
685	M	Admit for renal dialysis	0.9282	*2.6*
686	M	Kidney & urinary tract neoplasms w MCC	1.7237	*5.4*
687	M	Kidney & urinary tract neoplasms w CC	1.0441	*3.7*
688	M	Kidney & urinary tract neoplasms w/o CC/MCC	0.6867	*2.2*
689	**M***	**Kidney & urinary tract infections w MCC**	**1.1300**	***4.3***
690	**M***	**Kidney & urinary tract infections w/o MCC**	**0.7693**	***3.2***
691	M	Urinary stones w esw lithotripsy w CC/MCC	1.5454	*3.0*
692	M	Urinary stones w esw lithotripsy w/o CC/MCC	1.0690	*1.7*
693	M	Urinary stones w/o esw lithotripsy w MCC	1.4186	*4.1*
694	M	Urinary stones w/o esw lithotripsy w/o MCC	0.6879	*2.0*
695	M	Kidney & urinary tract signs & symptoms w MCC	1.2773	*4.2*
696	M	Kidney & urinary tract signs & symptoms w/o MCC	0.6615	*2.5*
697	M	Urethral stricture	0.8225	*2.5*
698	M*	Other kidney & urinary tract diagnoses w MCC	1.5681	*5.1*
699	M*	Other kidney & urinary tract diagnoses w CC	0.9890	*3.5*
700	M*	Other kidney & urinary tract diagnoses w/o CC/MCC	0.7026	*2.6*

DRG		MS-DRG Title	Weight	*GMLOS*
707	S	Major male pelvic procedures w CC/MCC	1.8265	*3.0*
708	S	Major male pelvic procedures w/o CC/MCC	1.2928	*1.4*
709	S	Penis procedures w CC/MCC	2.1038	*4.0*
710	S	Penis procedures w/o CC/MCC	1.3429	*1.5*
711	S	Testes procedures w CC/MCC	2.0316	*5.5*
712	S	Testes procedures w/o CC/MCC	0.9580	*2.3*
713	S	Transurethral prostatectomy w CC/MCC	1.3814	*3.3*
714	S	Transurethral prostatectomy w/o CC/MCC	0.7402	*1.7*
715	S	Other male reproductive system O.R. proc for malignancy w CC/MCC	2.2268	*5.5*
716	S	Other male reproductive system O.R. proc for malignancy w/o CC/MCC	0.9629	*1.5*
717	S	Other male reproductive system O.R. proc exc malignancy w CC/MCC	1.7495	*4.9*
718	S	Other male reproductive system O.R. proc exc malignancy w/o CC/MCC	0.8786	*2.3*
722	M	Malignancy, male reproductive system w MCC	1.6031	*5.3*
723	M	Malignancy, male reproductive system w CC	1.0532	*3.9*
724	M	Malignancy, male reproductive system w/o CC/MCC	0.5501	*1.8*
725	M	Benign prostatic hypertrophy w MCC	1.2644	*4.4*
726	M	Benign prostatic hypertrophy w/o MCC	0.7159	*2.8*
727	M	Inflammation of the male reproductive system w MCC	1.4106	*4.8*
728	M	Inflammation of the male reproductive system w/o MCC	0.7821	*3.2*

DRG		MS-DRG Title	Weight	*GMLOS*
729	M	Other male reproductive system diagnoses w CC/MCC	1.1196	*3.7*
730	M	Other male reproductive system diagnoses w/o CC/MCC	0.6266	*2.2*
734	S	Pelvic evisceration, rad hysterectomy & rad vulvectomy w CC/MCC	2.5547	*4.6*
735	S	Pelvic evisceration, rad hysterectomy & rad vulvectomy w/o CC/MCC	1.1910	*1.9*
736	S	Uterine & adnexa proc for ovarian or adnexal malignancy w MCC	4.2211	*10.1*
737	S	Uterine & adnexa proc for ovarian or adnexal malignancy w CC	2.0310	*5.3*
738	S	Uterine & adnexa proc for ovarian or adnexal malignancy w/o CC/MCC	1.2602	*2.9*
739	S	Uterine,adnexa proc for non-ovarian/adnexal malig w MCC	3.1647	*6.5*
740	S	Uterine,adnexa proc for non-ovarian/adnexal malig w CC	1.5819	*3.1*
741	S	Uterine,adnexa proc for non-ovarian/adnexal malig w/o CC/MCC	1.1470	*1.8*
742	S	Uterine & adnexa proc for non-malignancy w CC/MCC	1.4972	*3.0*
743	S	Uterine & adnexa proc for non-malignancy w/o CC/MCC	0.9903	*1.7*
744	S	D&C, conization, laparoscopy & tubal interruption w CC/MCC	1.5084	*3.9*
745	S	D&C, conization, laparoscopy & tubal interruption w/o CC/MCC	0.8514	*1.9*
746	S	Vagina, cervix & vulva procedures w CC/MCC	1.3694	*3.0*
747	S	Vagina, cervix & vulva procedures w/o CC/MCC	0.8814	*1.6*
748	S	Female reproductive system reconstructive procedures	1.0096	*1.5*
749	S	Other female reproductive system O.R. procedures w CC/MCC	2.6239	*6.1*
750	S	Other female reproductive system O.R. procedures w/o CC/MCC	1.0854	*2.2*

DRG		MS-DRG Title	Weight	*GMLOS*
754	M	Malignancy, female reproductive system w MCC	1.9784	*5.8*
755	M	Malignancy, female reproductive system w CC	1.0880	*3.7*
756	M	Malignancy, female reproductive system w/o CC/MCC	0.6334	*2.1*
757	M	Infections, female reproductive system w MCC	1.5292	*5.7*
758	M	Infections, female reproductive system w CC	1.0452	*4.2*
759	M	Infections, female reproductive system w/o CC/MCC	0.6995	*3.2*
760	M	Menstrual & other female reproductive system disorders w CC/MCC	0.8063	*2.8*
761	M	Menstrual & other female reproductive system disorders w/o CC/MCC	0.4904	*1.8*
765	S	Cesarean section w CC/MCC	1.1125	*3.9*
766	S	Cesarean section w/o CC/MCC	0.7766	*2.9*
767	S	Vaginal delivery w sterilization &/or D&C	0.9235	*2.7*
768	S	Vaginal delivery w O.R. proc except steril &/or D&C	1.0976	*3.1*
769	S	Postpartum & post abortion diagnoses w O.R. procedure	2.1785	*4.3*
770	S	Abortion w D&C, aspiration curettage or hysterotomy	0.7070	*1.6*
774	M	Vaginal delivery w complicating diagnoses	0.7137	*2.5*
775	M	Vaginal delivery w/o complicating diagnoses	0.5625	*2.1*
776	M	Postpartum & post abortion diagnoses w/o O.R. procedure	0.7075	*2.5*
777	M	Ectopic pregnancy	0.9550	*1.6*
778	M	Threatened abortion	0.5247	*1.9*

DRG		MS-DRG Title	Weight	*GMLOS*
779	M	Abortion w/o D&C	0.4843	*1.5*
780	M	False labor	0.2515	*1.2*
781	M	Other antepartum diagnoses w medical complications	0.7568	*2.7*
782	M	Other antepartum diagnoses w/o medical complications	0.4463	*1.6*
789	M	Neonates, died or transferred to another acute care facility	1.5258	*1.8*
790	M	Extreme immaturity or respiratory distress syndrome, neonate	5.0315	*17.9*
791	M	Prematurity w major problems	3.4363	*13.3*
792	M	Prematurity w/o major problems	2.0734	*8.6*
793	M	Full term neonate w major problems	3.5299	*4.7*
794	M	Neonate w other significant problems	1.2494	*3.4*
795	M	Normal newborn	0.1692	*3.1*
799	S	Splenectomy w MCC	5.0639	*9.9*
800	S	Splenectomy w CC	2.5234	*5.2*
801	S	Splenectomy w/o CC/MCC	1.5980	*2.8*
802	S	Other O.R. proc of the blood & blood forming organs w MCC	3.1642	*7.7*
803	S	Other O.R. proc of the blood & blood forming organs w CC	1.8831	*4.7*
804	S	Other O.R. proc of the blood & blood forming organs w/o CC/MCC	1.1558	*2.3*
808	M	Major hematol/immun diag exc sickle cell crisis & coagul w MCC	2.2217	*6.1*
809	M	Major hematol/immun diag exc sickle cell crisis & coagul w CC	1.1901	*3.8*

DRG		MS-DRG Title	Weight	*GMLOS*
810	M	Major hematol/immun diag exc sickle cell crisis & coagul w/o CC/MCC	0.8226	*2.7*
811	**M**	**Red blood cell disorders w MCC**	**1.2488**	***3.6***
812	**M**	**Red blood cell disorders w/o MCC**	**0.7985**	***2.6***
813	M	Coagulation disorders	1.6433	*3.6*
814	M	Reticuloendothelial & immunity disorders w MCC	1.6910	*4.9*
815	M	Reticuloendothelial & immunity disorders w CC	0.9844	*3.3*
816	M	Reticuloendothelial & immunity disorders w/o CC/MCC	0.6655	*2.4*
820	S	Lymphoma & leukemia w major O.R. procedure w MCC	5.8779	*13.0*
821	S	Lymphoma & leukemia w major O.R. procedure w CC	2.4025	*4.8*
822	S	Lymphoma & leukemia w major O.R. procedure w/o CC/MCC	1.2336	*2.2*
823	S	Lymphoma & non-acute leukemia w other O.R. proc w MCC	4.4850	*11.3*
824	S	Lymphoma & non-acute leukemia w other O.R. proc w CC	2.1684	*5.9*
825	S	Lymphoma & non-acute leukemia w other O.R. proc w/o CC/MCC	1.2935	*2.9*
826	S	Myeloprolif disord or poorly diff neopl w maj O.R. proc w MCC	4.9280	*10.8*
827	S	Myeloprolif disord or poorly diff neopl w maj O.R. proc w CC	2.2746	*5.3*
828	S	Myeloprolif disord or poorly diff neopl w maj O.R. proc w/o CC/MCC	1.3642	*2.7*
829	S	Myeloprolif disord or poorly diff neopl w other O.R. proc w CC/MCC	3.1769	*6.7*
830	S	Myeloprolif disord or poorly diff neopl w other O.R. proc w/o CC/MCC	1.2781	*2.4*
834	M	Acute leukemia w/o major O.R. procedure w MCC	5.3828	*10.3*

DRG		MS-DRG Title	Weight	*GMLOS*
835	M	Acute leukemia w/o major O.R. procedure w CC	2.1606	*4.6*
836	M	Acute leukemia w/o major O.R. procedure w/o CC/MCC	1.2240	*2.9*
837	M	Chemo w acute leukemia as sdx or w high dose chemo agent w MCC	6.0485	*15.6*
838	M	Chemo w acute leukemia as sdx w CC or high dose chemo agent	2.8181	*6.7*
839	M	Chemo w acute leukemia as sdx w/o CC/MCC	1.3175	*4.8*
840	M*	Lymphoma & non-acute leukemia w MCC	3.0843	*7.5*
841	M*	Lymphoma & non-acute leukemia w CC	1.6167	*4.8*
842	M*	Lymphoma & non-acute leukemia w/o CC/MCC	1.0830	*3.1*
843	M	Other myeloprolif dis or poorly diff neopl diag w MCC	1.7768	*5.3*
844	M	Other myeloprolif dis or poorly diff neopl diag w CC	1.1701	*4.1*
845	M	Other myeloprolif dis or poorly diff neopl diag w/o CC/MCC	0.7830	*2.8*
846	M	Chemotherapy w/o acute leukemia as secondary diagnosis w MCC	2.4337	*5.7*
847	M	Chemotherapy w/o acute leukemia as secondary diagnosis w CC	1.1062	*3.0*
848	M	Chemotherapy w/o acute leukemia as secondary diagnosis w/o CC/MCC	0.8635	*2.5*
849	M	Radiotherapy	1.4239	*4.6*
853	**S***	**Infectious & parasitic diseases w O.R. procedure w MCC**	**5.3491**	***11.1***
854	**S***	**Infectious & parasitic diseases w O.R. procedure w CC**	**2.4891**	***7.0***
855	**S***	**Infectious & parasitic diseases w O.R. procedure w/o CC/MCC**	**1.5849**	***3.6***
856	S*	Postoperative or post-traumatic infections w O.R. proc w MCC	4.7874	*10.1*

DRG		MS-DRG Title	Weight	*GMLOS*
857	S*	Postoperative or post-traumatic infections w O.R. proc w CC	2.0412	*5.7*
858	S*	Postoperative or post-traumatic infections w O.R. proc w/o CC/MCC	1.3115	*3.9*
862	M*	Postoperative & post-traumatic infections w MCC	1.8903	*5.6*
863	M*	Postoperative & post-traumatic infections w/o MCC	0.9845	*3.8*
864	M	Fever	0.8441	*2.9*
865	M	Viral illness w MCC	1.7351	*4.9*
866	M	Viral illness w/o MCC	0.7855	*2.9*
867	M*	Other infectious & parasitic diseases diagnoses w MCC	2.6139	*6.8*
868	M*	Other infectious & parasitic diseases diagnoses w CC	1.0775	*4.0*
869	M*	Other infectious & parasitic diseases diagnoses w/o CC/MCC	0.7406	*2.9*
870	**M***	**Septicemia or severe sepsis w MV 96+ hours**	**5.9187**	***12.5***
871	**M***	**Septicemia or severe sepsis w/o MV 96+ hours w MCC**	**1.8527**	***5.1***
872	**M***	**Septicemia or severe sepsis w/o MV 96+ hours w/o MCC**	**1.0687**	***4.1***
876	S	O.R. procedure w principal diagnoses of mental illness	2.8172	*7.5*
880	M	Acute adjustment reaction & psychosocial dysfunction	0.6388	*2.2*
881	M	Depressive neuroses	0.6541	*3.2*
882	M	Neuroses except depressive	0.6953	*3.2*
883	M	Disorders of personality & impulse control	1.2682	*4.7*
884	M*	Organic disturbances & mental retardation	1.0060	*4.0*

DRG		MS-DRG Title	Weight	*GMLOS*
885	M	Psychoses	1.0048	*5.4*
886	M	Behavioral & developmental disorders	0.9173	*4.2*
887	M	Other mental disorder diagnoses	0.9795	*2.9*
894	M	Alcohol/drug abuse or dependence, left AMA	0.4509	*2.1*
895	M	Alcohol/drug abuse or dependence w rehabilitation therapy	1.1939	*9.1*
896	M*	Alcohol/drug abuse or dependence w/o rehabilitation therapy w MCC	1.5146	*4.7*
897	M*	Alcohol/drug abuse or dependence w/o rehabilitation therapy w/o MCC	0.6824	*3.2*
901	S	Wound debridements for injuries w MCC	4.0316	*9.3*
902	S	Wound debridements for injuries w CC	1.7077	*4.9*
903	S	Wound debridements for injuries w/o CC/MCC	1.0527	*3.1*
904	S	Skin grafts for injuries w CC/MCC	3.1738	*7.2*
905	S	Skin grafts for injuries w/o CC/MCC	1.2475	*3.2*
906	S	Hand procedures for injuries	1.2228	*2.4*
907	S*	Other O.R. procedures for injuries w MCC	3.9235	*7.7*
908	S*	Other O.R. procedures for injuries w CC	1.9485	*4.4*
909	S*	Other O.R. procedures for injuries w/o CC/MCC	1.2150	*2.5*
913	M	Traumatic injury w MCC	1.1683	*3.7*
914	M	Traumatic injury w/o MCC	0.7110	*2.5*
915	M	Allergic reactions w MCC	1.4721	*3.6*

DRG		MS-DRG Title	Weight	*GMLOS*
916	M	Allergic reactions w/o MCC	0.5139	*1.7*
917	**M***	**Poisoning & toxic effects of drugs w MCC**	**1.4093**	***3.5***
918	**M***	**Poisoning & toxic effects of drugs w/o MCC**	**0.6346**	***2.1***
919	M	Complications of treatment w MCC	1.7206	*4.4*
920	M	Complications of treatment w CC	0.9779	*3.1*
921	M	Complications of treatment w/o CC/MCC	0.6522	*2.2*
922	M	Other injury, poisoning & toxic effect diag w MCC	1.5088	*4.0*
923	M	Other injury, poisoning & toxic effect diag w/o MCC	0.6620	*2.2*
927	S	Extensive burns or full thickness burns w MV 96+ hrs w skin graft	16.4534	*22.3*
928	S	Full thickness burn w skin graft or inhal inj w CC/MCC	5.7744	*11.9*
929	S	Full thickness burn w skin graft or inhal inj w/o CC/MCC	2.2090	*5.1*
933	M	Extensive burns or full thickness burns w MV 96+ hrs w/o skin graft	3.2785	*2.6*
934	M	Full thickness burn w/o skin grft or inhal inj	1.6045	*4.2*
935	M	Non-extensive burns	1.3909	*3.2*
939	S	O.R. proc w diagnoses of other contact w health services w MCC	3.1182	*6.6*
940	S	O.R. proc w diagnoses of other contact w health services w CC	1.7675	*3.7*
941	S	O.R. proc w diagnoses of other contact w health services w/o CC/MCC	1.3403	*2.2*
945	M*	Rehabilitation w CC/MCC	1.3804	*8.3*
946	M*	Rehabilitation w/o CC/MCC	1.2037	*6.5*

DRG		MS-DRG Title	Weight	*GMLOS*
947	M*	Signs & symptoms w MCC	1.1324	*3.6*
948	M*	Signs & symptoms w/o MCC	0.6897	*2.6*
949	M	Aftercare w CC/MCC	1.0038	*2.8*
950	M	Aftercare w/o CC/MCC	0.6005	*2.3*
951	M	Other factors influencing health status	0.8578	*2.4*
955	S	Craniotomy for multiple significant trauma	5.4056	*7.2*
956	S*	Limb reattachment, hip & femur proc for multiple significant trauma	3.8321	*6.8*
957	S	Other O.R. procedures for multiple significant trauma w MCC	6.7306	*9.7*
958	S	Other O.R. procedures for multiple significant trauma w CC	3.8734	*7.3*
959	S	Other O.R. procedures for multiple significant trauma w/o CC/MCC	2.5391	*4.3*
963	M	Other multiple significant trauma w MCC	2.6733	*5.5*
964	M	Other multiple significant trauma w CC	1.3904	*4.1*
965	M	Other multiple significant trauma w/o CC/MCC	0.9824	*3.0*
969	S	HIV w extensive O.R. procedure w MCC	5.4896	*12.0*
970	S	HIV w extensive O.R. procedure w/o MCC	2.2785	*4.9*
974	M	HIV w major related condition w MCC	2.6335	*6.7*
975	M	HIV w major related condition w CC	1.3383	*4.7*
976	M	HIV w major related condition w/o CC/MCC	0.8627	*3.3*
977	M	HIV w or w/o other related condition	1.1194	*3.6*

DRG		MS-DRG Title	Weight	*GMLOS*
981	S*	Extensive O.R. procedure unrelated to principal diagnosis w MCC	4.9319	*10.1*
982	S*	Extensive O.R. procedure unrelated to principal diagnosis w CC	2.8504	*5.9*
983	S*	Extensive O.R. procedure unrelated to principal diagnosis w/o CC/MCC	1.7462	*2.8*
984	S	Prostatic O.R. procedure unrelated to principal diagnosis w MCC	3.4143	*9.3*
985	S	Prostatic O.R. procedure unrelated to principal diagnosis w CC	1.8859	*5.1*
986	S	Prostatic O.R. procedure unrelated to principal diagnosis w/o CC/MCC	1.0389	*2.1*
987	S*	Non-extensive O.R. proc unrelated to principal diagnosis w MCC	3.3422	*8.4*
988	S*	Non-extensive O.R. proc unrelated to principal diagnosis w CC	1.7554	*4.8*
989	S*	Non-extensive O.R. proc unrelated to principal diagnosis w/o CC/MCC	1.0430	*2.3*
998	-	Principal diagnosis invalid as discharge diagnosis	0.0000	*0.0*
999	-	Ungroupable	0.0000	*0.0*

S = Surgical DRG
M = Medical DRG
*Post-acute care transfer DRG
GMLOS = Geometric mean length of stay

Flap- "advancement" →
Free a layer of tissue and "Stretch" to fill a defect.

Hypertension:
- Essential
- Hypertensive Heart Dis
- " CKD
- " Heart & CKD
- Secondary Hypertension

Cirrhosis: include manifestations
- ascites
- encephalopathy
- portal hypertension

(cause_cholestatic, alcohol)

Non viral Hepatitis: (alcohol, autoimmune)
Acuity - acute, subacute, chronic